Adam laid his lips tenderly against hers. He felt the wetness of tears on her cheeks and was momentarily startled, but as she wound her arms about his neck and her lips flared to life beneath his, they were forgotten. With the barriers he himself had erected to keep them apart no longer able to withstand the onslaught of his own desires, he allowed himself the pleasure of holding her, exploring her trembling body with knowledgeable hands, plying her mouth with unrestrained kisses. He wanted this girl as he had wanted no other in his life before. Caution was thrown aside; and his cardinal rule discarded alongside. His fingers reached for the plait of red-gold hair, and began to unbraid it . . .

Valentina Luellen was born in London in 1938, and educated in Gloucestershire and London. She began writing at school—mainly because she loathed maths! It took her twelve years of writing before she had a book accepted, but she has now had over 40 stories published. Historical romances are her favourite to write, because she loves researching into so many different countries, learning about customs and costumes and the way people lived hundreds of years ago.

Valentina Luellen and her husband moved to Portugal six years ago when he became seriously ill. There his health began to improve and they now live in a renovated farmhouse on the Algarve with their 19-year-old son, 21 cats, two Portuguese dogs, and around 100 trees—almonds, olives, figs, plums, lemons and oranges —most of which they planted themselves.

WHERE THE HEART LEADS

Valentina Luellen

MILLS & BOON LIMITED
15–16 BROOK'S MEWS
LONDON W1A 1DR

First published in Great Britain 1986
by Mills & Boon Limited

© Valentina Luellen 1986

Australian copyright 1986
Philippine copyright 1986

ISBN 0 263 75467 7

Set in 10 on 11 pt Linotron Times
04–0786–76,300

Photoset by Rowland Phototypesetting Limited,
Bury St Edmunds, Suffolk
Made and printed in Great Britain by
Cox and Wyman Limited, Reading

CHAPTER ONE

'Is HE not the most handsome man you have ever seen?' Alida asked her sister from behind a nervously fluttering fan.

A slender eyebrow winged upwards as Natália focused her full attention on the two men who had just entered the room, more than a little surprised at the statement. Her elder sister had been widowed for just one year and had solemnly vowed never to become seriously involved with another man again—a sentiment not shared by their father, who was already looking for a suitable replacement for her.

Not because her marriage had been a happy one—far from it. Natália knew that the nine months she had been married had been the most miserable of her life. Now here she was showing an interest in one of the many English officers who had been fighting for the past two years to liberate Portugal and its unhappy people from the tyrannical domination of the French emperor, Napoleon. Most of the war had been fought in Spain against overwhelming numbers, but for the past winter months of 1809 and into the spring of the following year they had withdrawn behind carefully constructed lines of defence in the heart of her country, to rest and replenish their resources. A welcome relief after the bloody battle they had fought in July 1809 at Talavera, south-west of Madrid, when the French had lost over ten thousand men!

On the lips of every Portuguese man and woman who listened eagerly for news—Natália among them—was the name of Sir Arthur Wellesley, the brave English commander who had, it was reported, faced an enemy force of forty thousand men with less than a quarter of that number under his command—and won! For this brilliant victory he was created Viscount Wellington by his sovereign, George III.

Natália was forced to admit that Alída's choice of companion was infinitely better than the man chosen by their father. Both men wore the striking blue and gold uniforms of cavalry officers. She had seen so much varied apparel passing through the small village of Alto Verde these past months, as weary men spent their time in the surrounding towns or the capital, Lisboa, that she was becoming quite an expert on the different regiments. One man was tall and fair, the pale skin deeply freckled by the strong Portuguese sun which dealt unmercilessly with those unaccustomed to its strength. The other was very tall—a good head above his companion and anyone else present, who were mostly neighbours and close friends of her father—like most Portuguese homes, theirs was always open to offer hospitality, to the passing English soldiers—and so handsome she was momentarily robbed of speech. His appearance had set many a female heart racing, she saw, by the furtive glances cast towards him when duennas were looking elsewhere, the soft giggles and whispered comments behind feathered fans fluttering as agitatedly as Alída's was doing as she continued to gaze at them. Thank goodness their father had his back towards them and was conversing with friends, so that he did not see her reaction to these new arrivals! He had vowed, after her husband had been killed fighting in Spain, never to have a soldier as a son-in-law again.

Natália felt her own heart beating rather unsteadily, for the tall stranger was the kind of man every young girl wove fantasies about, and she was no exception. Compared with the man she was soon to marry, he was Adonis; a proud young god—devastatingly handsome —to be worshipped from afar!

He was very sure of himself, she mused, considering the touch of arrogance in the way he held his head and regarded the other guests. A pair of gleaming eyes swept the room, and a smile touched the lean mouth as he considered each young woman who passed in front of him with an effrontery that was breathtakingly blatant.

What kind of man had Alída found for herself, and where? This was the first she had heard of a beau, although her sister did live in Mafra, where there was an English garrison. The man's gaze came across the room to rest on her. Not on Alída, of that she was sure, but on *her*. For one heart-stopping moment she could not breathe. When she tried to swallow, there was a restriction in her throat which made it impossible. She tried to avert her eyes from the bold stare which began at the dainty satin shoes just visible beneath the hem of her gown and continued slowly up over the clinging skirts of her saffron velvet gown, past her tiny waist to the fullness of her breasts above the high-waisted bodice. She had borrowed one of Alída's newest gown in the latest 'Empire' style made famous by Frenchwomen. She harboured no love for the French, but she did like their clothes, especially the simple classic styles which her sister had brought back with her from Lisboa. It was also just a little daring and naughty, baring more of her full breasts than was usually modest, and that in itself had been sufficient to prompt her into wearing it. It was different.

By the time those eyes reached the red-gold tresses swept high onto the crown of her head and secured with a yellow ribbon to match her gown, her cheeks were flushed with uncomfortable colour. She had never known a man's interest to affect her so.

'He's coming to speak to me,' Alída whispered. 'Where is Father? He mustn't see us together.'

'Nonsense!' Somehow Natália dragged her eyes away from the two figures threading their way across the crowded room. 'You may speak with whom you please. After all, you are hostess here tonight. Besides, you can do anything you like, and Father will never rebuke you. It's only me he delights in making miserable! How I wish I were free . . .'

Natália did not miss the sympathetic glance which came her way before her sister's attention was once more returned to the approaching officers. She had always been the favourite. When their father deigned to show a scrap of affection, Alída could do no wrong, but then she was always polite and obedient, like their mother. Never a word of rebellion, or one tiny sign of reproach that he had forced her into an unhappy marriage. How different they were—and yet, strangely enough, close enough to have been born as one.

Natália had been betrothed to Cesar João Ferreira Duarte when she was six years old. Almost as if her father had been wishing to be rid of her even at that tender age, she had often thought. All her life she had been groomed and prepared for the day when she would be his wife. The wife—the property of a man twice her age. Had not Alída been unexpectedly widowed, and the usual mourning period to be observed, she would already be married—perhaps a mother. She inwardly shuddered . . . At the thought of being touched by Cesar's fat hands, or because the two men had halted before them, and those gleaming eyes once again dwelt on her face?

'Drew.' The name was little more than a sigh on Alída's lips as she lifted her hand and it was taken—not by the dark-haired man, but by his companion. 'It's all right, this is my sister Natália. She will keep our secret. I fear I rather gave myself away when I saw you come in. You were so sure you would not be able to get leave.'

'We've been assigned special duties in Lisboa for the next month. And some relaxation.' The young face split into a wide grin as he eyed the man at his side. 'You haven't met my brother, have you? Also my commanding officer. Adam, this is Alída. Isn't she all I said she was? And Natália, whose debt I am in for sharing her sister's confidence.'

'Everything—and more,' came the quiet reply from the other, and Alída blushed profusely as he brushed his lips across her fingertips. 'I haven't heard Drew speak of anyone—or anything—this past month but this vision of loveliness he has encountered. Now I understand his enthusiasm to be here tonight. Dona Natália, I am honoured.'

The hand which clasped Natália's was cool to the touch, yet no sooner had he paid her the same courteous gesture than she quickly pulled herself free, every nerve in her body tingling with the brief contact. What was the matter with her? She was nearly eighteen, a child no longer, but a full-grown woman—and about to become a wife. She had no right to feel anything for a stranger, and certainly not one with bold eyes and a casualness of manner which indicated that he thought himself capable of having any woman in the room he chose. And he spoke Portuguese—they both spoke it—so beautifully!

Close to, she saw that his skin was deeply tanned, unlike that of his brother, which seemed to indicate he had been in her country for some considerable time. It was not merely a surface tan brought on by the summer sun either, for here it was almost spring, and it still remained to enhance those aquiline features. The eyes were a mixture of green, flecked with hazel and a touch of grey, with firm black brows arching above them. The thick hair was cut short without a single grey strand. The mouth was firm, as was the jawline. Not a man easily swayed by others, she decided. A man of strength and decision—a born leader. She found it difficult to judge his age. He could have been in his late twenties or into the mid-thirties. When he smiled, it could have been the former, yet she noticed a hardness about the eyes, where tiny white lines seared the bronze skin, that made her decide he was at least thirty.

Cesar was forty-two, so what did age matter? Aware of the questioning look which sprang to his eyes at her scrutiny, she floundered for words, and stammered,

'Are—are you on leave, senhor? You have some strange men with you—I mean, they looked so rough.' It was a struggle to regain her composure. No man had ever affected her so.

'I command a force of "irregulars", senhorita. *"Guerrilleros"* as the Spanish call them, and most of my men are from Spain. We are on our way to Lisboa in the hope of recruiting more Portuguese to join us.' The answer had a certain reluctance about it as if he did not like to discuss his activities. 'When Drew and I return to headquarters, no doubt we shall find new orders awaiting us to take us back into the field. I, for one, shall be glad. We have been idle for too long.'

'Idle, the man says!' His brother gave a snort. 'The French haven't allowed us to sit about and do nothing. Ever since we entrenched behind the lines, they've plagued us like flies. It's time we showed them a thing or two'.

'Don't,' Alída murmured. 'I can't bear to think of you in the midst of fighting.'

Adam's eyes narrowed slightly as Drew reached out and gently squeezed her hand. He did not approve of his brother's deepening relationship with her. In time of war, a soldier's thoughts should be on staying alive, not on some woman left behind. Distracted men were dead men! A little on the plump side, she was nevertheless a pretty little thing with a shy air that he knew would appeal to Drew the moment they met, for he also suffered from the annoying affliction of being easily embarrassed in company.

Adam never allowed anyone to bother him—at least, not so that it showed. It took a great deal to irk him, although the temper he had inherited from an Irish grandmother raised its head more than he cared to admit; over the years, he had learned to control it. When he was roused, however, he was a bear—a veritable devil whose anger encompassed all about him and often led him into the distasteful situation of demanding satisfaction from whoever had upset him.

His companions during his years of soldiering had discovered it was wise to stay out of the way of this master of sword and pistol when he was in a bad temper, and never to approach him on any pretext when he was in a foul mood. Thus they could retain a valuable friendship, for, despite this shortcoming, Adam was popular with his men and possessed many friends among his fellow officers.

He found Alída's sister, Natália, something else entirely—young and beautiful beyond words! He realised he had not taken his eyes off her since he came into the room. She was aware of it, too. He was sure she followed his every move. It was rare to find such boldness in a well-brought up Portuguese girl.

Her eyes were the most startling blue he had ever seen, like huge flawless sapphires set off to perfection by smooth white skin. Petal soft, he suspected, and kept well away from the scorching summer sun. It would be protected as carefully as she was, day and night, probably by the old duenna hovering at her elbow. Nobody would get past that one! Like most Portuguese women, her life would be ruled by strict convention. Was she was bored as other women he had met in Lisboa, he wondered? Bored, and willing to break a few of those rules—as Alída was doing?

As his eyes considered her, she quickly averted her gaze. It came to him that she was little more than a child playing at being a woman, despite all her finery and jewels. He would be a fool to indicate the slightest interest in her. It was his rule never to become involved with single women—only mature ones whose more worldly leanings allowed them to continue with their own lives once the first fires of ardour had waned. Besides, he did not consider it fair to marry and leave a wife while he went off to fight. Neither would he allow any woman of his to accompany him to war, as so many other men did. War was a man's occupation; women belonged at home with their sewing and their family.

Aware of Drew giving him a puzzled look, he realised he had been staring pointedly at Natália for several minutes without speaking. He knew he would never hear the last of it if his brother suspected he was in any way attracted to her! With a faint shrug of his shoulders, he said,

'Don't worry, Dona Alída, my brother bears a charmed life. Besides, the angels don't want that ugly face among them! Before I leave, would it be possible for you to introduce me to whoever has made this overnight sojourn here so enjoyable? Your people have always been most friendly towards the English, yet I am still touched at how readily they have opened their doors to welcome our men wherever they go. My brother will have great difficulty in dragging himself away from here. He is finding the hospitality quite . . . irresistible.'

'Senhor!' Alída protested softly. 'If you cause me to blush any more, my father will be wanting to know the reason. He is your host—the *juiz*, the judge, in Alto Verde. It was his wish that you and your men, indeed all British soldiers who pass through our village, should be made to feel welcome. You are all a long way from home, and our two countries have been allies for many centuries. Friends should not be turned from one's door—ever. I think we should introduce you to him now, before his curiosity brings him to us. Don't you agree, Natália?'

'*Sim*,' her sister replied, acutely conscious of the

curious looks she had been receiving from Dona Margarida, her ageing duenna, for the past five minutes. She could not even smile politely at a man without her companion suspecting that the worst was about to happen. She would cluck her tongue in the most disapproving fashion, like some old hen! Marriage would at least do away with the necessity for her to be chaperoned every minute of the day, her every movement spied upon. In two short months her freedom would be curtailed by a jailer of a different kind—her husband! Despite the warmth of the room, she shivered.

Swiftly she thrust the unpleasant thought to the back of her mind, as she became aware that Adam was extending his arm towards her and waiting for her to place her hand on it so that he might escort her in the wake of Alída and Drew, who were already moving away. Tentatively she laid slender, ringed fingers on the blue sleeve with its gold cuff, managing to smile faintly as she fought to control the tremor which went through her at the contact. If she acted like a child, he would take to his heels and run like a scalded cat, to seek solace with some woman who returned his bold stares candidly, with a promise of her company in full red lips and tantalising glances—perhaps more.

Dare she, who had never allowed any man to take liberties with her—not even Cesar, who was soon to be her husband and her master and who made it plain each time they were together that he expected her to refuse him nothing   play such a game?

Natália longed for some exciting adventure to take her away from the *quinta* where she had been born and raised and spent every day engaged in the small dull routine. She rose and had breakfast, then sat with her tutors for the remainder of the day, reading, sewing, playing the piano—all the things a young lady should know. Most of all how to be a dutiful wife . . . and mother. Certainly she did not feel old enough for any of these things to appeal to her.

Why was it all necessary, anyway, when everyone told her she had inherited all her mother's fine qualities? Marietta Sedália Alicia Lareira had been a gracious lady, loved by all, the daughter of a high-born land-owner from Porto, endowed with beauty, simplicity, charm . . . Natália had all of these and something more —a hint of recklessness which did not fit well into the otherwise modest character. Where that originated from, no one knew—or would tell her!

She had always thought what a perfect match her father had made for himself. A docile woman, who had obeyed his every wish until the day she died and deprived the Quinta das Reposeiras of a kind and benevolent mistress, and him of an irreplaceable wife. Neither daughter had ever succeeded in growing close to him. Both had discovered, at an early age, that they were not what he had wished for. He had prayed for strong sons to inherit his name, his power and the land. In his view, women were good only for marriage and for the provision of heirs. He barely acknowledged their exist-ance while they were children, leaving them in the care of governesses and duennas, sour-faced spinsters who never understood Natália's sudden flashes of high spirits and independence and sought to beat them out of her, when all other methods failed.

Natália disagreed with her father's sentiments most strongly, but she would never have said so to his face, or in his hearing. For seventeen years she had been a good and dutiful daughter who had learned all Abílio had demanded of her—oh! those endless hours of study when she could have been walking in the vineyards or riding free like the wind across the sun-baked earth —who had become betrothed to the man chosen for her, and suffered in silence a terrible agony of mind. She did not want to be saddled with a family before she had known what it was like to live! She was not a brood mare!

She wanted freedom to express herself, to go where she pleased.

She had seen Alída married to a man she did not love, lose a child before it was due to come into the world because of the cruelty of her drunken husband, and had comforted her through the long days afterwards until her health returned, praying that she would not have to experience this kind of hell in her own marriage. Now her sister was a widow, free of the chains that had held her, until such time as their father decided she should marry again. Alída lived in a house in the town of Mafra that had belonged to her husband, a compulsive gambler. It had been the only thing left to her when he died. All money had been frittered away on the turn of a card, and she had been hard pressed by creditors until their father had intervened to pay all the outstanding bills.

Now Don Abílio was pressing her to return to the *quinta*, to keep him company, as Natália would soon be married and going away. Cesar's home was near Setúbal in the north. Stubbornly Alída had resisted the temptation to return to the family fold, knowing well how she would be completely dominated once again by his will if she did so. Natália was glad that she had not, for she often went to stay with her for a few days, experiencing beneath her roof a sense of freedom never possible at home. She was glad of the slightest excuse to be out of her father's sight; and with Alída, a respectable widow, as her chaperon it was possible to leave behind the dour Dona Margarida. How she would miss her sister's gay chatter!

The man who turned to watch the two young women cross the room was of medium height, immaculately dressed in dark grey, a spotless white shirt accentuating the swarthiness of his features. The brown eyes narrowed for a moment as they considered his two daughters, missing nothing: neither the swiftness with which

Alída disengaged herself from the grasp of the man accompanying her, nor Natália's agitation. Her cheeks were quite flushed, and she found it impossible to look at her father. A soft sigh escaped him as he smoothed the lace ruffles of his sleeve over hands that had seen many days of back-breaking toil. An influx of handsome men to complicate his life further was something he could well do without. Natália was safe—she was betrothed, and Dona Margarida would allow her no foolish escapades. But Alída . . . It was time she married again and gave him grandchildren to bounce on his knee. She was not unattractive, and a fine dowry and lands would be provided as before. Soon, he mused, raising his eyes to the face of the young officer at her side, and seeing the look of obvious adoration mirrored on his face before his interest was noticed and quickly veiled.

'Father, will you allow me to introduce you to two of the British officers who are to stay overnight in our village?' Alída said quietly.

Natália was amazed at her composure. Their father had a way of making them both feel insecure and uncomfortable when he chose. With her, it seemed to be all the time. Always he watched her, as though waiting for her to do something which would displease him. She had given up trying to love him. Since he had announced her betrothal to Cesar, she felt as if she had died inside—the life had gone from her body, and she had no interest in what went on around her. And then an *estrangeiro*—a foreigner—had looked at her, and she had remembered how it had been before all her dreams had been shattered.

Adam straightened and bowed smartly. Drew hesitated, then followed his example.

'Major Adam Sorrell, senhor. My brother, Captain Drew Sorrell. You have no cause to remember me, but we did meet briefly in Lisboa last month, at a reception given for the English ambassador at the home of Lady Cecilia Lambert.'

'I remember you quite well, Major. I was told at the time that you commanded a band of Spanish *guerrilleros*, and had fought with considerable bravery—not to mention savagery—and some unorthodox methods that your superiors were frowning over for months!'

'You have an excellent memory, senhor,' Adam replied coolly.

'You have these men here with you now, at Alto Verde?'

'The priest was kind enough to give them shelter in one of the church outhouses. It will suffice for them until we move on. The villagers will not be inconvenienced in any way, Senhor . . .'

'Lareira. Abílio Armandio Maria Lareira.' The name was supplied with pride, and a faint smile etched the corners of Adam's mouth as he eyed the man. Not as pompous as he looked, he suspected. There was a shrewd brain lurking behind those active eyes, which threw a quick reproving glance at Alída for not having introduced him correctly. She flushed and lowered her gaze to the polished wood floor. 'I am the *juiz* in Alto Verde. I am sure your men will give no trouble, Major Sorrell—unruly as they seemed to be when I saw them ride through the village. Surely not all of them are Spaniards?'

'I have a few Portuguese riding with me. All good men . . . good fighters. As you say, somewhat unorthodox, but then it is not always possible to apply rules and regulations to the game of war. I am aware that your countrymen are not altogether well disposed towards their neighbours; however, as you do hold a position of importance, senhor, I should be grateful if you would pass the word among your people that we wish for no ill feelings between any of us. These men have fought on your behalf, often under extremely difficult circumstances, and deserve to be treated with the same respect afforded to your own countrymen.' Adam gave a stiff, curt bow. There was anger in his eyes, and he did not bother to conceal it. 'If you will excuse me, I have just seen someone I know come in.'

'I think I have upset the Major,' Abílio murmured, a deep frown wrinkling his brows as he stared after the tall figure. 'It was unintentional.' He looked apologetically at Drew, who came immediately to his brother's defence.

'The *guerrilleros* who ride with my brother have no families, Senhor Lareira. Wives, children, fathers and mothers have been murdered by the French. I do not think I need to explain further, and distress the ladies.'

'No, Captain. I know very well the atrocities committed by the enemy. I lost a brother to their Dragoons at the Battle of Talavera. They found him wounded with a dozen other comrades, and . . .' A flicker of pain momentarily entered those brown eyes; then it was gone, and he was once more composed. Natália knew nothing more than that her uncle had been killed in action, and now began to wonder what dreadful thing had taken place for her father to show even a minute lack of control. He was always so calm, so unemotional, that she often thought him a cold man, unable to care or love anyone. And then, at times like this, rare occasions, when she saw something flicker beyond the placid expression, she wondered if she really knew him at all.

Drew nodded sympathetically, relieved that Adam's abrupt departure had been smoothed over.

'And the Portuguese with you?' Abílio asked.

'They too have lost some, if not all of their loved ones. It has proved an incentive to fight like the devil. With the French more often than not outnumbering us two to one with both men and cannon, we need men like that.'

'That I can understand. We, too, have our own resistance fighters, brave men who risk much to bring information on the enemy to the right quarters. I have even heard a rumour that many young Irish novices from our universities have enlisted as volunteers to carry information. Brave young men indeed. I do find it —unusual—however, that an Englishman commands a band of *guerrilleros*.'

'My brother has lived in Portugal most of his life, senhor, which is why he speaks your language fluently, as well as Spanish. He was a perfect choice. His love for this country is no less than that of any Portuguese. He considers it his own, and wishes to protect it according-ly.' Drew smiled as he supplied the information. He was very proud of his brother's total involvement in the war, his passionate desire to free his adopted country from Napoleon's tyranny.

'And you, Captain Sorrell, do you share in this wish? Of course you must, or you would not be with him.'

'I hope, when this is all over, to return to my medical studies, senhor. I am a doctor, not a soldier, although I confess to indulging in more fighting than healing since I arrived here last year. My brother has a rule never to leave wounded behind him, as he has seen too often what happens to them. That is where I try to make myself useful.'

'I am sure you are most competent, Captain,' Abílio replied, slightly turning away in a manner which seemed to indicate that he wished to move on. 'As able in your chosen profession as I am certain your brother is in his.'

'Well!' Slowly Drew relaxed. Alída laid a hand on his arm, thankful that their father had at last left them. She had grown exceedingly hot and uncomfortable during the conversation, afraid he might insist on his daughters accompanying him while he chatted with his guests. 'Not a good first impression, I would say. Adam didn't help by going off like that, but he did have his feathers ruffled by your father's observations.'

'Why?' Natália asked curiously. Her eyes scanned the

room and found Adam Sorrell beside the long dining-table which had been laid with cold food, and wine from their own vineyards. He was talking, smiling, all his attention centred on an attractive dark-haired woman who was standing close to him. Very close, she noticed, and wondered why it annoyed her to see some strange female fluttering her eyelashes at him. He was nothing to her!

He seemed to look younger when he smiled. The tiny crinkle-lines at the sides of his eyes disappeared and his mouth softened, to ease a little the firmness of the jawline. It was a strong face, but growing old before its time, she decided. The face of a soldier who had witnessed terrible things, fought in bloody battles, probably been wounded. Her curiosity was mounting rapidly, yet she knew she could not question Drew directly about his brother. Interest in the war was another matter. After all, it concerned everyone . . .

'The task of my brother and his men is to stay ahead of the main cavalry and act as scouts, sending back information on enemy movements and maps of the terrain. He is more at home in this countryside than anywhere else on earth,' Drew explained, unaware of the anxiety mounting on Alída's features as she listened. 'They do not wear uniforms which would betray them to the French, and this makes it easier to penetrate their lines. There are times when my brother looks more like a peasant than an English gentleman. Believe me, you would never recognise him out of his blues!'

'And you are with him,' Alída breathed. 'I cannot bear it! Could you not ask for a transfer to another unit? Something less dangerous? Why must you risk your life so recklessly?'

'To answer that, I would have to show you the horrors of a battlefield strewn with dead and dying men, my sweet Alída, and I will not do that as I have no wish to give you nightmares.' Drew's hand covered hers, and squeezed it reassuringly. 'Did Adam not tell you that I bear a charmed life? I do. Nothing is going to happen to me, because I intend to ask your father for your hand the moment this war is over. I shall woo you—and charm him, to the best of my abilities—and make you my wife.'

Natália caught her breath at the look which came into his eyes as he looked at her sister. Tenderness—such as she had never seen in a man before. And her heart ached a little more to know she would never experience such devotion. Cesar was as cold and practical as her father. It was an arranged marriage, and she knew what was expected of her—what they expected of her. To fulfil her duties as wife and mother, be meek and obedient, subservient to the will of her husband. To run the house and instruct the servants, while always leaving the final word to the master. Alída threw her a searching look as she shivered.

'Look! Even Natália fears for your safety. We shall talk no more of war and death. Alto Verde saw too much of it when the French were here.' She broke off, not wishing to relate what had taken place.

It was Natália who said quietly, 'They came looking for food and horses . . . took all we had not hidden. Abused several of the village girls, and when their fathers or brothers objected, hung six of our men in the village square. Had it not been for the arrival of a senior officer, they would have broken into this house. They were very drunk . . .' She crossed herself, pushing the ugly memory of those bodies in the square to the back of her mind. 'They did not . . . And they left the next day, but it is not something any of us here will forget. You must understand my father's concern.'

'I'll explain to Adam,' Drew assured her. 'There will be no trouble.'

Several times during the evening, as Natália mingled with the other guests, she was seized with an urge to stop beside Adam Sorrell and engage him in conversation, but Dona Margarida dogging her footsteps every moment was a deterrent which averted a second meeting. He was never lost for a companion, she noticed, and seemed to mingle with surprising ease. How long had he lived in Portugal—and where? Lisboa? Was that why he chose to take his leave there? Perhaps he had a wife —surely he must at least have a mistress! He was too attractive a man to be alone. What kind of woman would please him? One as sure of herself as he was, she decided, watching him from behind her fan as he passed by with his brother. To her surprise, he looked towards her, acknowledging her with a faint nod of his head before joining her father to partake in a glass of vintage port from his select stock in the cellars. The French had not realised the treasure-trove in wine they had missed by not entering the *quinta*.

Natália moved about the room, always positioning herself while engaged in conversation in such a way as to be able to watch him. He moved well for a man of his height and build. She followed strong hands with long brown fingers as they sketched something in the air by way of explanation for the men listening to him. Drew had called him a gentleman, yet he chose to do his fighting behind enemy lines and out of uniform. To be caught meant death—or to be shot as a spy, if he was lucky. Torture and agony at the hands of his captors more likely, she thought, as she once again remembered the blackest day in the memory of her village. The French were not known for their kindness and mercy. Alída would pray for Drew Sorrell in her prayers. She would pray for his brother.

A glass of sparkling white wine in her hand, she found herself—not without design—behind a screen of potted plants. She paused to linger by the french windows, which opened on to the summer patio where even now, after an appalling winter with heavy snow, deep purple bougainvillaea twined thickly in and out of the archways and climbed to the wrought-iron balcony outside her room. Dona Margarida, thankful for a moment's rest, sank into a chair and, within seconds, Natália saw her eyelids begin to droop. She did not move. She dared not, for she did not want to awaken her, or to alert the two men a few feet away of her unwarranted interest—in one of them.

'Well, what do you think?' she heard Drew remark, casting a speculative eye around the room.

'Have you a particular subject in mind? Alída, for instance? You have made by far the best choice.' Adam's voice was mildly amused. Natália felt a tingle run down her spine at the deep tones.

'And I intend to keep her, brother, so hands off! What about her sister, Natália? There's hidden fire in that one, mark my words.'

'A very charming child.' This accompanied by a low chuckle. 'Good Lord, Drew! While I admit she's stunning to look at and, as you say, possessing more than meets the eye, are you suggesting that I snatch her from her cradle? Why, she can't be more than sixteen.'

'Seventeen; almost eighteen. I did my homework, in case you are interested.'

'And as innocent as a new born babe? Thank you, but she's not for me! I have no intention of being called out by an irate father over . . . over some child-woman with fascinating eyes. I'm leaving now. I'll make my excuses to Senhor Lareira and get back to the men. The wine and food have been excellent, but I want to put my feet up and get a good night's rest. A full night's sleep wouldn't do you any harm,' Adam added, eyeing the dark circles of fatigue beneath his brother's eyes. They barely showed on his own sunburnt skin, despite the fact that he had not allowed himself to sleep completely for over a week. The habit of sleeping with one eye open, the brain still alert for trouble, was a hard habit to break, even when he found himself in safe surroundings among friendly people.

Well, almost friendly. The slur Abílio Lareira had cast on his *guerrilleros* still rankled. What did he, living in his fine house, waited on by servants know of their hardships? A few French soldiers had invaded his village and murdered a few men, and he thought it was the end of the world! God help him if the Lines of Torres Vedras were ever penetrated and the full force of Napoleon's élite, veterans all, swept down upon him and his peaceful existence! He left without noticing the red-cheeked, silently fuming girl staring after him with burning eyes.

'A charming child.' Could he not see she was a woman? 'As innocent as a new-born babe.' She was that, all right. She knew what was expected of her on her wedding night, but was there more that her duennas thought not suitable to tell her? She would never love Cesar, so how would she feel when he laid claim to her? Why could no one tell her that? Why did she feel this strange excitment when Adam Sorrell spoke, or touched her? She was no flirt; she did not make eyes at any man who came her way, as the village girls often did. She had watched them in the vineyards when no one was supervising their work—chasing each other in and out of the casks of wine, hugging and kissing. How could it be wrong, when they enjoyed it so?

Alída would know . . . She would ask her.

CHAPTER TWO

IT WAS well after midnight that Natália retired to her room and Dona Margarida, after seeing her mistress undressed and settled in bed, withdrew to her own small adjoining dressing-room. She was so tired she could not keep her eyes open, and was relieved that the tall officer with the grey-green eyes had not accepted the generous invitation of Dom Abílio to spend the night beneath his roof. It was bad enough for one of them to be sleeping so close to her charge, although she had noticed that many times that evening, *his* eyes had been for one woman only—in another direction, *graças a Deus!*

Natália had no intention of sleeping until her questions had been answered. She waited patiently until loud snores sounded from the other side of the door before throwing aside the bedclothes and reaching for her robe.

'Where are you going?' an urgent whisper demanded from the bottom of the bed. It was Pilar, Natália's maid. As protective as any mother, she always slept on a pallet on the floor, stubbornly refusing to be budged from this highly favoured position. Dona Margarida had protested and complained, for she did not like this swarthy-skinned woman who looked like a gipsy and was indeed said, by the villagers, to possess not only second sight but great healing powers. Pilar, in return, ignored her. The continual snubs and lack of politeness from a woman of lowly birth frequently sent the duenna into swooning fits. However, when it became clear that both girls adored her and that she was, at times, the only one who understood Natália's bouts of high spirits, Dona Margarida settled into an uneasy alliance with the woman.

In the light of the candle burning on a table, Pilar's face was softened by the glow, lessening the leathery look which always returned in the light of day. Perhaps in her mid-forties, she had been Natália's maid since her tenth birthday. Between them existed a friendship far more meaningful than any the girl had so far experienced in her life. Pilar was maid, friend, adviser—sometimes even mother. During the past turbulent years, as Natália fought within herself to discover an identity other than the one thrust upon her by her father, teachers and duennas, Pilar was always at her side with words of advice, often of comfort. Many times Natália had been held in the thin arms and rocked like a baby until her fears dispersed. Pilar knew the secrets of her heart, her dreams—and did not laugh at them like Alída or her father would have done—talked of strange places she had been to as a child, heightening Natália's interest in a world beyond the *quinta*—watched over her like a lioness caring for a new cub. To her Natália gave the affection she would have given to her true mother had she lived—the affection her father refused to accept in her early childhood, rejected as emotional and childish now she was a full-grown woman. If only *he* had once held her in his arms, and comforted her . . .

'Go back to sleep. I have to talk with Alída.'

'What is it she can tell you that I cannot?' A dark eyebrow rose quizzingly at the words. 'Why do you not ask Pilar what is in your heart?'

'Have you ever been married?' Natália asked in a hushed tone, as she belted a velvet robe about her. The night air was chill, and she shivered while looking about for her slippers. Pilar dropped them beside her feet and pulled the neck of the robe together beneath her chin with a disapproving frown.

'Foolish *menina*,' she reproved. 'Do you want to catch a cold? You will not be able to make eyes at the tall one if you are confined to bed.'

'I didn't . . . I mean—you haven't answered my question.' Natália was glad of the shadowy room which did not betray her flaming cheeks. Sometimes she thought Pilar could not only read her mind, but see into her very soul!

'Have I had a man? Are you still worried about Cesar? Or is there another reason for such a question?'

'Don't tease me, Pilar! I felt, tonight when I saw Adam Sorrell . . . I can't even explain it. I have never known such feelings. I am confused . . . and afraid . . . He looked at me as . . .'

'He looked at you the way any man looks at a woman he finds desirable,' Pilar murmured. 'But he is not for you.'

'Why do you say that? Because I am betrothed to Cesar? I know it is wrong to look at another man, but he is different! I can feel it here.' Natália laid a hand over her heart, which even now was beating quite rapidly because she was thinking of him.

'He has fire in his blood, not water! It would be unwise of any woman to rouse a man of his temperament if she did not intend to share his bed. She would probably end up in it, anyway. He is all man, that one. A fine-looking man!'

'You—you think he is attractive?' Natália stared as she looked at her maid. She saw amusement, and yet something more, as she gazed into the large brown eyes. Knowledge—that was what was there. It was what she lacked. In her opinion, Pilar could do no wrong. She found in her a loyal companion and friend, and she trusted her judgment.

Alída had once been her friend. Dear sweet, shy sister. How alike she was to Drew Sorrell! They were good for each other, and her heart rejoiced that she might have found a man to fulfil *her* dreams, but it sank as she considered their father's reaction to the liaison. A soldier for a son-in-law would not be his choice. A man with probable death as his only future. Abílio Lareira wanted grandchildren—that was his dream.

'Your sister is not in her room,' Pilar said quietly, as Natália moved towards the door.

'Not . . . ?' She caught her breath in surprise. 'Where is she?' She knew the answer before the confirmation came.

'With the other one. In *his* room.'

'Oh.' Natália went back to the bed, then, as the sound of singing came to her, she crossed to the window and peered out curiously. Whatever had possessed Alída to take such a foolish risk? One whisper to Father, and there would be a terrible row! He might even beat her for such disgraceful behaviour beneath his roof.

'She is in love,' Pilar said, standing close beside her and looking out across the street to the church, which stood clearly visible in bright moonlight to the right of the main house, beyond the encircling wall. It was only a small stone affair, and there had been plans to build a new, bigger place for the villagers to worship, but this had to be delayed when war came to ravage the land and take men off to fight.

'Shall I ever know what that is?' Natália asked. There were men sprawled in front of a blazing fire or seated on wooden crates or large boulders. Adam Sorrell's *guerrilleros*, she realised. They did not look so fierce and frightening now, as they talked and laughed among themselves, or listened to the melancholy song being rendered with great emotion, telling the story of a man who went off to war and returned to find that his sweetheart had married another. Now he had no reason to live and wished to die. Could anyone really feel that way? To love someone so fervently that life became unimportant if that love was lost?

A woman's laughter came out of the darkness, and then one of the village girls leaped into the flickering firelight, to wheel and spin before the gathering. First one man joined her, then others, and several more women appeared, until the fire was almost obliterated from Natália's view by the dancers. Strains of a guitar floated to her, the sharp staccato of castanets, shouts of approval as another *garrafa* of wine appeared. Someone sampled the *caldo verde*, a nourishing soup of vegetable stock, rich with slices of smoked garlic sausage, which was cooking in a large cauldron over the fire, and pronounced it ready. Earthenware bowls were grasped by eager hands. When they were filled, one of the men thrust a pan of chestnuts to the edge of the coals so that they could be heating while they enjoyed the soup, into which was dunked enormous chunks of freshly baked bread.

And then she saw him! Adam Sorrell was leaning against one of the outbuildings, arms folded across his chest. He had discarded his jacket, and the sleeves of his shirt were rolled back above the elbow to reveal bronzed arms dark with hair. He was tapping one booted foot against the other as he listened to the music, obviously enjoying it, and far more relaxed than when he had been in the house. Did he prefer the company of such rough fellows to that which had been offered him? She had overheard her father inviting him to stay in the house, the chance to sleep in a fine feather bed, but he had politely refused, saying that his arrangements had already been made. Drew had not refused, and now she knew why!

From a pocket Adam produced a long black Spanish *cigarrillo*, and proceeded to light it, cupping his hands about the flame of the match so that the wind did not blow it out. Then, with a comment that brought much laughter from his men, he thrust his hands deep into the pockets of his trousers and sauntered away from the fire—towards the *quinta* itself, pausing to cast an eye over the horses in the stable as he passed the open doors, the forge and the long, low building where the grapes were trodden in harvest time. For a man who had declared himself in need of rest, he was showing little inclination to retire.

A girl came running over the cobble-stones in his wake and spoke to him, laying a hand on his arm as if to induce him to return to his companions. Natália saw him shake his head, and she returned alone.

'He, too, is particular in his choosing,' Pilar observed.

Natália glanced sharply into the dark features, feeling her cheeks begin to burn uncomfortably as she recalled the conversation she had overheard.

'He called me a child!' she said in a low, fierce, indignant whisper which brought a gleam to the maid's eyes. 'A charming child!'

Adam had stopped beside the fountain almost beneath her window, to watch the stream of water emitted from the gaping mouth of a stone vixen with three tiny cubs nestled at her feet. Then, without warning, he raised his head, his gaze sweeping upwards—as if considering the mass of purple flowers climbing the walls of the house. Higher still, until Natália was sure his eyes were centred on the window where she stood.

She found herself unable to move, even though she realised the light from the candle at her side was allowing him a most revealing picture of her in her nightclothes. Again that strange restriction in her throat, the trembling in her limbs as she imagined the mockery in those grey-green eyes. A strangled cry broke from her lips and she stepped back to the bed, but not before she had seen him sketch a mock bow in her direction. The arrogant conceit of the man! A gentleman would never have acknowledged her presence and caused her embarrassment. Did he think, because she had looked his way more than once, that she found him interesting?

Aware of Pilar's scrutiny, she threw off her robe and climbed into bed without a word. The maid tucked the bedclothes about her and once again retired to her blankets at the base of the bed. Natália's head swam, and sleep evaded her for many hours as she relived the embarrassment of what she had heard, experienced humiliation and anger such as she had never known before as she considered Adam's amused comments to his brother.

Tomorrow she would show him she was no child, but a woman! And when she had forced him to admit his error, she would have the satisfaction of hearing him apologise. He would not smile then!

She was drifting into blessed sleep, when she remembered he had also said she had fascinating eyes . . .

Grinding the remnants of his *cigarrillo* underfoot, Adam stepped into the room where Nuno, his Portuguese servant, had laid out some of his personal possessions, pausing on the threshold to smile slightly at what awaited him. The room had been bare when he arrived, a cell sometimes used by visiting monks. Bare whitewashed walls with only a crucifix on one of them to alleviate the starkness. A hard wooden bed, softer now with the addition not only of his blankets, but a single feather mattress. Beside this, a small pine table on which was a bottle of his favourite brandy, the silver chalice of Moorish craftmanship he had acquired while in Spain and used at all times, and a plate containing half a fried chicken. The floor had been swept clean, cobwebs brushed from corners, and there was a smell of orange-blossom wafting through the open window, which had been shuttered and barred when he had first seen it.

His jacket had been brushed and hung on a makeshift hanger fashioned from two twigs on a nail on one wall. A fresh shirt was laid out for the morning, and more casual clothes in which to wander through the village and countryside, should he choose to do so.

A thin-faced boy clambered to his feet, and was rewarded with a warm smile for his efforts.

'A vast improvement, Nuno! Thank you. Help me with my boots, will you? I'm foot-sore and saddle-sore. I don't know which part of me aches the most!'

'You want another bath?' came the eager question. Hours before, while Adam pulled off his travel-stained clothes and shook the dust from his thick hair, an ancient tub had been brought in by one of the *quinta* work-hands, followed by buckets and buckets of hot water. Where it had come from, he had not been able to discover at the time. Only a few minutes ago, however, one of his men had revealed that it was used to hold the pig-swill at feeding time. That accounted for the sicken-ing smell that had turned his stomach as he tried to settle into it, Adam realised. Nuno was an accomplished scrounger, a necessity to an army man, a plague on the lives of ordinary soldiers from whom he begged, borrowed or stole to provide for his master.

Remembering how he had sat, unable to sink his shoulders beneath the water, unable to move even his toes in the confined container, Adam grinned as he shook his head.

'Pour me some brandy, and then I'll go to bed. Why don't you go and enjoy yourself outside?'

'You sleep alone?' Nuno stared at him perplexedly. 'You don't want a woman tonight?'

'No, I don't want a woman to share my blankets, *moço*, nor do I want you extending such an invitation to the men. If I hear you have been making yourself a little extra money, I shall hang you by your toes and roast you over a very large fire. Do I make myself quite clear?'

'*Sim, chefe.*' Nuno always addressed him as the rest of the *guerrilleros* did. 'Do you have a woman in Lisboa? I have many friends you would like.' Nuno gave a know-ing wink.

'Maybe.' Adam was noncommittal. Despite the many problems Nuno had given him since he had discovered the boy stealing from him in Lisboa, he was fond of the cheeky-faced rascal. He had never discovered his true age—he doubted if the boy knew it. He thought him to be about fourteen, but it was difficult to access correctly, for years of living in back alleys, picking pockets as a profession, not to mention the appalling company in which he mixed, had added years to the brown, pock-marked face.

Adam thought they had possibly become good friends because they were alike. They had both seen death, suffered hardship, often hunger, and had learned at an early age to fend for themselves and not depend on others. To trust no one and rely only on their own judgment. It had served them both in good stead. Adam Sorrell was an officer of exemplary courage, a born leader who rode with his men, often in front, never behind them . . . and so had earned their trust and respect.

Nuno also was good at his chosen profession, as slick a thief as the best in the country, despite his youth, endowed with a tongue heavily coated with honey and sugar, coupled with the smile of an angel—and the mistrusting heart of a gutter-rat, which was why he had been able to survive in the conditions in which Adam found him.

The Major had been on his way back to the house, taking a short cut through the Alfama, the old quarter of Lisboa, where tiny, narrow cobbled streets were dark and deadly for those unsuspecting enough to venture into them. He knew what often lurked in shadowy doorways, and had been prepared for the two men who launched themselves at him with knives. He knocked one unconscious and disarmed the other, who then ran. He had been bending over the senseless man when Nuno, the third member of the trio, had slipped up behind him, intent on relieving him of his wallet while he was otherwise occupied. Nuno had ended upon the cobbles, nursing a very sore wrist, looking up into the face of a man whose eyes were as cold as death.

The boy was no coward. He lived among thieves and murderers in the alleys of the old city, prostitutes and beggars, and thought nothing wrong in his existence. Adam was to discover it was the only one he had known since his parents had died of the smallpox and left him alone at the age of seven. Beaten black and blue by the tyrannical old uncle who gave him shelter and worked him all hours God provided, he had run away to make a living on his own.

Adam still did not know why he had not turned the dirty-faced urchin over to the police. Instead, he had taken him home with him, fed him, forcibly marched him upstairs to take a bath, and held him in the water while two terrified maids scrubbed the grime from his thin body. Another burned his flea-infested rags. When Nuno's language became too profane to bear, he had stuffed a wet sponge in his mouth and kept it there until he was dried and attired in clean clothes. Removing it, he had been rewarded with a string of abuse that had made even his ears burn. He had turned the boy over his knee and administered a sound spanking until the oaths and gutter-language diminished, and the only sound was that of Nuno crying. For perhaps no more than the second time in his life, he suspected.

He had then given him several escudos and told him to leave. Or—and the boy had stared at him as if he had taken leave of his senses—he could remain in the household as his personal servant, and accompany him when he rejoined his unit later that month.

"Where there is an army, there is always food to steal from some fat officer who has too much,' had come the sarcastic retort, accompanied by a careless shrug of his pathetically bony shoulders.

'If you steal from me, I shall wring your neck,' Adam had told him, and one look into that bronzed face had confirmed that the words were no idle threat. As with

Adam, Nuno never knew what made him stay. He did not trust this kindness . . . he had not earned it. And no one gave anything for nothing! There had to be another reason for someone to be so pleasant to him.

He was to discover, in the months that followed, that work was what was expected of him. Long hours when Adam returned to his unit, of grooming the fine horse the officer always rode, shining the tack until he could see his face in it. Helping him with his toilet, making sure his clothes were always immaculate. Providing the small things which made life more pleasant while on the march. He did all these things well—if not grudgingly. As for providing for Adam's needs . . . That was a different matter. To a scrounger like Nuno, to pit his wits against other boys with the same intention, veteran soldiers who thought they could obtain everything because they knew it all—he was in his element. Adam never went without, and did not always enquire closely into the sources of his 'little necessities'. The bond of uneasy friendship became one of firm trust and loyalty. Nuno took great care with his pilfering so that he could never be traced back to Adam and so cause him embarrassment, and the latter paid him the great compliment before fellow officers of calling him the best and most efficient boy any army man could ever have—words which were never to be forgotten!

'Where did the chicken come from?' Adam asked casually, as he tore off a leg and bit into it appreciatively. It tasted of piri-piri, a hot Portuguese pepper which was ground and used for most dishes. Just the way it was prepared for him at home. For a moment his heart ached to think of what he had left behind—what could happen to the beautiful old house and orchards if the French returned to confiscate British property and imprison foreign residents. His father was old, and might never survive such harsh treatment. Abruptly he thrust personal worries aside and finished the leg. It was not wise to allow his thoughts to wander. To relax now, even in such pleasant surroundings as Alto Verde, would soften his brain for the day he knew he would be returning behind the enemy lines—and that was dangerous. For him and all those who rode with him. Time for sentiment when it was all over. 'And don't tell me it fell from the sky and landed at your feet! Did you steal it?'

'It came from the kitchen of the *quinta*, given to me by a very pretty little girl. I swear it!' Nuno reached for the other leg when Adam pushed his plate away and indicated that he should help himself. 'She said I looked half-starved. I told her my master beat me every day and kept me hungry so that I was too weak to run away from him. She is going to leave the back door open for me tonight—if I am still hungry.'

'Then I suggest you go and satisfy your hunger and let me get some sleep,' Adam advised with a grin. 'But keep your sticky fingers off things which don't belong to you, little squirrel!'

Stripping off his outer clothes, he stretched out on the cot, his hands folded beneath his head. Despite the chill in the air, he suffered no discomfort as he lay listening to the sounds of revelry coming from outside. Unlike his companions, he did not feel the cold so intensely. The winters in Portugal were nowhere near as severe as those he remembered as a child in England. He had suffered from chest colds for most of the six years he had lived there with Drew, before his mother had died and his father brought them to the warmer climate. Now he could not recall the last time he had gasped for breath.

His men were a hot-blooded, quarrelsome lot, he mused, as an angry voice reached his ears. He would intervene if the argument continued, for he wanted no trouble in Alto Verde. It was probably only some silly dispute over a woman's favours. However, a moment later, he heard renewed laughter, and the guitar-player began to strum his instrument with a lively tune. He relaxed again . . . and found a vision coming to his mind that brought a fierce frown to his face.

Now why was *she* in his thoughts? The sight of her standing at that upstairs window was not one he would forget in a hurry. The long, burnished hair falling past her shoulders to her waist made her look even younger than her eighteen years. Wasn't that what Drew had said? Seventeen—nearly eighteen. The soft glow of the candlelight at her side gave a touch of colour to that flawless alabaster skin. The urge to reach out and touch it had been almost irrepressible. He shook his head as if to dispel the image from his mind, but it remained with startling clarity.

Firm young breasts outlined beneath the clinging velvet robe which hugged a tiny waist and flared out over lithe hips. The fullness of those lips, the perfect bone-structure of her features which framed those large expressive blue eyes. What a colour they were! Rich as sapphires, so startling at first sight that they had taken his breath away. Was he mad? She was a child, and not for him! Drew was the romantic. *He* did not have one iota of romance in his soul! Love had never touched his heart. Most of his friends were married with families, and he knew that some felt sorry for poor Adam Sorrell who could not find the right woman. Idiots! He was not even looking. If one ever come along, he would know, but he was not seeking a wife and the ties of marriage. Not yet, anyway.

Others envied him his bachelor existence. Women seemed to find him attractive and were always near at hand when he needed company—or something more —but at the age of twenty-nine, none had ever held his attention for very long, and certainly not one had ever made him consider marriage. Yet this child-woman Natália, who had trembled when she touched him as if he were the very devil himself, plagued his thoughts and allowed him no rest.

Why had she been at the window? Seeking a lover? No, not with that stern man for a father. Wishing she was out in the cool night air with his men, perhaps? He sensed a certain disquiet about her which he could not put into words. An inner torment. A touch of fire. Perhaps Drew was right, and she did have a rebellious streak inside her. He would never know. Could she have been looking for him? No, why should she? He was just one of the many English soldiers who had passed and would be passing through Alto Verde in the very near future. Perhaps she had not been expecting to be ignored!

With a sigh he reached for his cigarettes, changed his mind, and poured himself a large brandy instead. One way or the other, he was going to sleep tonight, he thought, as he tipped the fiery liquid down his throat. It was the last of the bottles Nuno had brought with them from Spain. Fire leaped through his stomach. He grimaced and thought to remind the boy to get something more mellow. Even *aguardente*, a fig brandy distilled by most Portuguese, was better than this. His old Portuguese nanny had raised him on the stuff. Perhaps that was why he had not suffered a cold since. Hot water and *aguardente*. It was her answer to everything from the gripe to stomach cramps, and it never failed. The fire outside had died, and the men round it had crawled into their blankets, or wrapped themselves in *sarapes* for warmth, some experiencing such 'inner' warmth that they had not bothered to do even that, but had crept into the stables, amid the straw and horses, to sleep blissfully until the morning. Adam, however, despite consuming the best part of the new bottle of brandy, did not sleep for a long time . . .

Natália slept later than usual the next morning. The small porcelain clock on the bedside table had just struck nine when Pilar brought her customary glass of fruit juice and informed her that her father had already breakfasted and ridden off to the next village with some labourers to look at a bull he was thinking of purchasing.

'Is my sister up yet?' She was determined to have the conversation with Alída that had been denied her the night before.

To her chagrin, the maid replied, 'She went out with Captain Sorrell half an hour ago, to show him the countryside. They rode through the village towards Monte Verde.' Pilar moved about the room, putting away oddments of clothes draped over a chair, shoes still lying where they had been taken off the night before, adding, with a wicked smile on her dusky features, 'The other one has gone riding, too. I overheard him talking with Dom Abílio, who gave him permission to tour the vineyards. If you had been awake, perhaps you could have accompanied him.'

'With Dona Margarida dogging my footsteps!' Natália grimaced, quickly drank her fruit juice and sprang out of bed. If there was a chance of seeing Adam Sorrell alone, she was going to take it, but she would have to make it look as if the encounter was accidental.

'You won't have to worry about her this morning. She has had one of her fainting spells, and I have given her a cup of my *erva cidreira* tea. You know how that relaxes her and sends her to sleep.'

'Pilar, what would I do without you?' The woman possessed a wealth of knowledge in her head about so many things, including the medicinal properties of many herbs and wild grasses which flourished in the country-side. Dona Margarida would sleep like a baby for several hours. And with her father also out of the way . . .

'Do you think it wise to go after him, *menina*? He is like no other man you have ever met!' Pilar warned, helping her into her underclothes.

That is exactly why I want to be with him, she almost said, and stopped herself just in time, saying instead,

'He called me a child! I can't forget that. A charming child! I intend to teach him a lesson.'

'Beware he does not teach you one,' came the sombre reply. 'Perhaps I should ride with you?'

'No, I shall not be away from the house long. Should my father return before I do, say . . . say I have gone to church, and be waiting to warn me that he is here,' Natália said firmly.

She had no idea what kind of lesson she would inflict, or what she could do to make Adam Sorrell regard her in a new light, as she rode away from the *quinta* astride a dappled stallion Abílio had given her a few months after she became formally betrothed. The gift had surprised her, but before she could thank him for the magnificent animal which she immediately named Diabo, he had informed her that it was so that she could rid herself of the last shreds of the rebellion which still lingered over the forthcoming marriage. She could ride the horse into the ground for all he cared, so long as, when the wedding day came, she had resigned herself to the fact that her wild days were over. 'Wild days!' That was how he thought of her daily rides. He had seen her returning to the *quinta* one morning, racing ahead of the young stable-lad who had accompanied her, when Dona Margarida had suffered yet another 'spell'. Her hair had been streaming behind her in the wind, her usually pale cheeks glowing with excitement, and to the horror of the household who came out to watch her approach, she was riding astride, not side-saddle, so that her skirts and petticoats were hitched up about her knees to show a very large expanse of undignified hose. To make it worse, some of the village boys had urged her on with loud cries of encouragement, until a broom, wielded by one of their mothers, had forced them to take flight. For days, it had been the talk of the *quinta*. It was still remembered in the village, for she had raced past the tiny whitewashed houses like a whirlwind, leaving them all agape—but with smiles and warmth, for Natália was well liked by everyone. She rode like a man! What a pity she had not been a boy, the son Dom Abílio had prayed for!

There was very little she set out to accomplish which she did not succeed in doing—and doing well. She could speak Spanish and French passably, and read in both languages. Spoken English she could understand a little. She was versed in Portuguese arts and poetry, and enchanted her father's guests with her mastery of the piano. Yet he never congratulated her on her abilities, and frowned at those who compared her accomplishments with those of her mother. Would he have been so reticent had she been a boy? She had long since ceased to care, for he had never loved her. She did not know why, but she accepted it now. He was giving her in marriage to a man more than twice her years just so that he could have grandsons to inherit his home and lands. Never would he have considered sharing what he owned with his two daughters.

Outside the village, Natália reined in to look about her. It was a beautiful spring day. Wild irises were already beginning to bloom, spreading a blanket of blue and white across the bare landscape. The almond blossom was late this year, she noticed, as she turned her horse on to a back track and rode at a leisurely pace towards the mountains. A light breeze lifted the pink and white petals from the trees as she passed, and they fell about her head and shoulders like tiny snowflakes. Soon bright green leaves would take their place, and then the newly-formed almonds. She hoped it would be a good crop for everyone. Since the French came to steal and plunder, very few of the villagers had managed to put away much of anything for when times were hard.

Before Napoleon's desire to place either a staunch ally, or one of his family, on the throne of Portugal became a reality, and thousands of French soldiers invaded the country, the village had been self-sufficient and prosperous. Behind Alto Verde, on terraced slopes, groves of oranges and lemons, almonds and olives flourished in the hot summer sunshine and vines hung heavy with ripe black grapes. Nearly every house had its own small patch for growing vegetables—potatoes, onions, cabbages and turnips pushed their way to the light alongside wild geraniums and multicoloured blooming succulents.

Once there had been sheep and goats grazing on short, tufted grass, eating their fill of the thick clover, but only a few remained, for French patrols constantly passing by had depleted the flocks. Trees had been stripped, barns emptied and no thought given to how the villagers would survive the next harsh winter. Had it not been for the sacks of grain and dried vegetables put by in the *quinta* and miraculously saved from scavenging hands, the people of Alto Verde would have fared badly.

Her father had opened his cellars and distributed more than enough to see them through the unfriendly months ahead, when rain swept down from the mountains and washed away newly-planted seeds and tiny saplings, unable to withstand the force of the rushing water, which at times poured over the tiny cobbled streets and mud tracks in torrents. It was typical of him, Natália mused. Such kindness for those who worked for him, yet his own daughters were often treated as strangers.

Slowing the stallion's pace to an easy walk, she allowed her gaze to wander over the landscape in front of her. The ground was already hardening in the sunshine, the vines protruding from it stark and bare, but cut back and ready for new growth. Thousands upon thousands of vines which would produce juicy grapes, which in turn would be made into wine at the *quinta* and sent as far afield as England . . . once the war was over and normal trade resumed with Portugal. Her father, until that time came, refused to allow his precious kegs to be risked at sea. His warehouses in Lisboa bulged with an overflow, as did the cellars and outbuildings of the *quinta* itself. She liked harvest time, although it was the busiest season of the year. Friends came to visit and watch the grapes being trodden, to see the enormous wooden vats being stirred, to sample a glass of Abílio's finest produce. She would miss the harvest here this year, for she would be married and living in Setúbal . . .

Abruptly her eyes clouded, and a tiny frown puckered the smooth line of her forehead. Now she had spoiled a pleasant ride with an ugly thought! She came upon Adam Sorrell reclining against a huge rock, his face upturned to the sun, so unexpectedly that she almost rode him down and quickly jerked on the reins to pull the horse aside. Swift as her reaction was, his was quicker as he spun away out of danger with the agility of a mountain cat. He had been hidden by a thick expanse of olive trees which bordered one side of the vine. Near one of them stood his horse. His uniform had been discarded for a pair of hide breeches and high leather boots. He wore no coat, and the sleeves of the thick shirt were pushed back almost to his elbows. A breeze tousled the crisp black hair, sending wisps of it curling about a tanned cheek.

'What—what are you doing here?' Natália said, the words coming out in a jerky manner which indicated her nervousness at the encounter. She had set out to find him, and now that she had, the very sight of him set her trembling.

'Your father very kindly gave me his permission to look over his vineyards. I am impressed,' Adam returned. Natália thought it would take more than the sight of bare vines to impress him! 'You are fortunate to live where you do, or all this could be lost.'

'Lost?' she echoed. 'How?'

'The British army, as you know, has been encamped behind our fortified lines at Torres Vedras all winter, but the French have not; so, to attempt to halt their advance further south, a scorched-earth policy has been adopted. The enemy must forage for their food, and I hear they are quite good at it, but they'll find damned little to steal now.'

'Which means they will search small villages like Alto Verde and hang innocent men just for hiding food for them, as they did here.' Natália's lips curled in disgust at his words. 'How do you expect people to live if you burn their crops and deprive them of their livelihoods? Farmers have to feed their families, Major Sorrell.''

'A great many families who have complied with our policy have been moved within the safety of the lines. That is partly why they were constructed. They are well taken care of, I assure you.'' Reaching into a pocket, he drew out a long black *cigarrillo* like the one she had seen him smoking the night before and lighted it.

As a cloud of blue-grey smoke spiralled into the air, he enquired, 'And what brings you out on this fine spring morning—are you searching for your escort, or have you eluded them?' His eyes considered the trim riding boots just visible beneath the hem of her blue skirt, then lifted to wander casually over the matching coat, cut snugly to her waist, the double row of gold buttons curving over her breasts, the bright yellow ribbon that pulled a mound of cascading curls into the nape of her neck. He had to admit that he liked what he saw. He had been surprised and annoyed at the ease with which she came unbidden into his mind, and had vowed to stay well out of her way until he left the next day. Now here she was, within touching distance again. And he wanted to touch her, Adam acknowledged. What kind of spell was she weaving over him? He was no foolish boy to be attracted to a pair of blue eyes.

'Why should I wish to—elude—my duenna?' Natália

replied, a soft laugh escaping her. She could not help herself.

'I have seen her, remember? A veritable dragon! Besides, it must be inconvenient, at times, to have her dogging your footsteps. Not that you would act— indiscreetly—when alone. I am sure you have been brought up too well!'

Well enough to know she should not be alone with a strange man even for a few minutes, Natália thought. Was he laughing at her? Did he suspect she had deliberately followed him? There was laughter dancing in those grey-green eyes, and she floundered for words as he straightened and came to her, to offer her his hand.

'Would you like to get down for a while? I have some cheese in my saddlebags that we could share.' What was he doing? Inviting her to stay, when he should have bade her a polite 'Bom dia', and ridden on his way.

Natália nodded. She could not bring herself to speak. Was anyone watching them? Dare she linger, to satisfy her curiosity about this man? He was so different from last night; perhaps he did find her attractive. Why else would he seek to delay her?

'He looked at you the way any man looks at a woman he finds desirable,' Pilar had told her. Was she desirable? 'He has fire in his blood, not water!'

She came sliding out of the saddle into strong arms which did not release her once she was on the ground. Her upturned face was close to his. So close that she felt his warm breath on her cheek. As her lips parted, she heard him draw a sharp breath and then his hold on her was tightening, his head bending towards hers. Too late she realised what he meant to do.

At the touch of his lips on hers, she stiffened with shock in his embrace. His kiss contained a rough passion which kindled a flicker of fear in her. He might consider her a child, but that did not stop him from treating her as he probably did all the other women he fancied. Before

Adam Sorrell, only Cesar had held her so tightly and demanded that she submit to his kisses. When she was in his arms, he was no gentleman, but even his searching hands had not aroused this kind of fear in her. Fear, not because she disliked what was happening to her, but because she liked the sensation he had stirred within her. It was new—and exciting!

She must not like it—or him—and never must he realise what disturbing thoughts were running through her brain. With a gasp, she tore her mouth free, at the same time pushing against his broad chest with clenched fists.

'Let me go this instant! Are you mad? I am not one of those girls who—who allows any man to touch her.' I am betrothed, she almost said, but the words froze on her lips as Adam's eyes narrowed simply. His arms fell away from her and he stepped back. He looked almost embarrassed, and then a smile touched his mouth, and the hazel flecks dancing in his eyes mocked her indignation.

'Mad? A little, perhaps. Why are you angry? I was under the impression that you wanted me to kiss you. Did I ruffle your feathers by calling you a child last night? Oh, yes'—he gave a chuckle, as bright colour stained Natália's cheeks—'I knew you were there. People who eavesdrop never hear good of themselves, didn't you know that?'

'You—you said it deliberately—to make me angry?' He was insufferable. Her eyes blazed, and for a moment she considered slapping him, but it would have been a pointless gesture and nothing would be gained by it . . . except a smarting palm.

Adam considered her in silence for a long moment, drawing deeply on his *cigarrillo* as he watched her blushes. He seemed to be fighting some inner conflict with himself, she thought, as the dark brows drew together. Then, extinguishing his cigar beneath a booted heel, he demanded with an insolent twist to his lips.

'Where you hoping to hear me say that I find you irresistible? I'm sure it has been said to you before —many times.'

'No,' she cried, and knew by the swiftness of her answer that she had not deceived him. Who would find her irresistible? He was mocking her again!

'A woman who does not want to be flattered! What an unusual child you are.'

'I am not a child!'

'Indeed you are not,' Adam returned, as brilliant fire flashed from her eyes. 'Nor are you a full-grown woman. Do not play games with me, *menina*.'

'I don't know what you mean!' Natália understood very well. He believed she had gone out of her way to find him and to arouse his interest in her—as, indeed, she had. Never before had she wanted a man to pay attention to her . . . never had she thrilled to a man's touch as she did when Adam Sorrell touched her. Never had she wanted to be more knowledgeable, like Pilar and Alída. In a few short hours he had turned her world upside down. She was confused by her own emotions —hurt by his rebuff and his mockery, and yet she had only herself to blame, she realised. What did such a man want with her?

'I accept that you do not—and perhaps it is better like that. I am a jealous man. I would not share your affections with another. Not even a single smile, however innocent,' Adam answered. What did one so young and innocent know of the hunger of the heart? The way the smiles, the sweet words of a pretty girl could touch the heart of a lonely man, especially a soldier. He had told himself he did not want the chains of marriage, to be bound to one woman. He had plans for when the war was over . . . to return to his father's business. To return to England, to meet old friends and visit places he had not seen in five years. So many dreams of his own home, not yet realised. When all this was done, he might think of taking a wife . . . and then he had taken Natália in his arms and kissed her, and for one mad moment nothing had mattered. She had fired his blood as no other woman had, and yet he ridiculed her for being a child. For her defence—or his? he wondered. In a gentler tone, he sought to warn her that others who might follow after him, and be received beneath her father's roof, might not look on her in the same light. They would see beauty and innocence and seek to take it from her.

'You are like a little fledgling bird, eager to try out new wings. Take care you do not fall and hurt yourself, little bird.'

'You talk in riddles,' Natália exclaimed, wishing with all her heart she had never left the house. She had made a fool of herself. How he would enjoy relating this encounter to his brother! And what if he mentioned her foolishness to her father? 'I think I shall continue with my ride.'

'Not alone. I shall accompany you back to the *quinta*. Unless you would care to ride on further with me? I am meeting Drew and your sister at the *tasca* on the hill road. I believe the wine there is worth sampling.'

'It is—it comes from my father's vineyard,' Natália replied stiffly, being careful not to hold too tightly to his arm as he assisted her to mount. 'I shall not detain you further. Have no fear that anyone can catch me on Diabo.'

'A brave boast for one so young!'

Had he not made her feel insignificant, incapable of achieving anything worth while, as she was often made to feel in her father's company, Natália would probably have allowed him to ride with her, knowing that propriety demanded she have an escort of some kind. As it was, the taunt roused the wildness in her that everyone in the household had tried so hard—and unsuccessfully —to curb. Rebellion blazed from her lovely features as she snatched the reins up into one slender hand.

'Catch me then—if you can!' she challenged.

Adam jumped back as she urged the stallion forward. As he ran for his own mount tethered beneath an olive tree a few yards away, he glimpsed a flurry of white petticoats and a long expanse of pale woollen stockings as Natália, with the devil inside her urging her on to prove herself yet again, flung her leg across the saddle. She had forgotten her father's wrath on the last occasion she rode like a man, the tears and shame she endured shut alone in her room for two days without even Pilar's presence to comfort her. She had only one thought in her mind—to reach the hilltop *tasca* before Adam Sorrell.

Workers in the fields looked up, startled, at the two fast approaching riders, and stood open-mouthed as they flashed by. Some, recognising not only the stallion but the dishevelled, wind-blown girl astride him, bent low across his back, her young face bearing the most determined of looks, shook their heads and crossed themself and said a prayer that Dom Abílio would not see his daughter being pursued by a strange man. It was plain she was not running away from him, or she would have called to them for help. Perhaps it was a contest. She would win. No one in Alto Verde could outride Natália Maria Lareira!

The bite of the wind stung Natália's cheeks. She had lost the ribbon from her hair almost the moment she started, and the red-gold mass of curls tossed in wild confusion about her shoulders. She gave the stallion his head, confident she would reach the *tasca* first. She not only had the best horse outside Lisboa, but she knew the way through every tiny cut-through and twisting track that wound in and out of the carob trees and flowering almonds. Petals showered her like snow, until she began to feel like the princess in the ancient legend of the Al-Gharb.

A princess from a distant cold land had come to Portugal to marry a prince, but was unhappy, for she missed the falling of gentle snowflakes, the touch of them against her skin, the frost on the ground. So in love with his bride was the prince that he could not bear to see her misery, and so, before his palace, he had planted hundreds of almond trees. In the spring, when the petals fell, the ground was covered in them and they resembled snow so much that the princess was never unhappy again.

Natália loved the legend. How romantic that a man should do that for love! Cesar did not have a romantic bone in his body. No man would ever consider her in such a fashion . . . The very first man she was attracted to had laughed at her—as Cesar laughed at her. One because she was a dreamer, the other because she was not woman enough for him. Could a woman not have dreams, even foolish ones? How inconsiderate and unfeeling men were!

She was dismayed to find, as she reined Diabo in to get her bearings and regain a little breath from the hectic ride, that Adam, far from being a long way behind, was racing towards her, and that the gap between them was minimal. She would have to ride like the wind if she was to beat him! Wheeling about, she urged the stallion up a steep incline, heading towards a short cut which would bring her out directly below their destination. It meant crossing an old river-bed that had not known water for years. She was aghast to discover a veritable torrent gushing over once dry stones and parched earth. The rains of recent weeks had filled it to within a few inches of the top of the bank.

She heard a shout behind her, half-turned, and saw Adam was waving at her madly. He wanted her to stop! And to let him gloat that she was afraid her horse was incapable of making it to the other side.

'Diabo, *meu bom cavalo*. Jump as you have never jumped before!' she whispered into an alert ear, and without further hesitation urged him on.

For a second he faltered, for one terrifying moment when her heart came into her mouth and she had a vision of being plunged into the water. Then with a jolt which knocked the breath from her body and threw her forward over his neck so violently that she almost pitched from his back, he landed safely on the far side. He had done it! She could have cried out in exaltation—had she possessed the breath. Without looking around, she headed him towards the whitewashed building just visible on the mountainside, but at a slower pace. She was trembling from head to toe, despite the satisfaction of her great achievement, only now realising the risk she had taken to thwart her pursuer.

As Adam caught up with her, she reined in and slid from Diabo's back, leaned against him, and declared in a tremulous voice,

"I did it! I won! I told you I could not be beaten.'

She was seized and shaken like a rag doll. She cried out, tears starting to her eyes, and was roughly shaken again until her teeth rattled.

'Idiota! Whatever possessed you to jump that water?' Adam shouted. The anger burning in his eyes startled her and extinguished any urge to retaliate against his ungentlemanly behaviour. Why was he angry? Because she had won, not he?

'I've come this way many times. There is no danger,' she protested, but not very forcefully, as she recalled how cold and frightening the water had looked as she passed over it. 'Diabo is a wonderful horse.'

'And you are a fool! I should put you over my knee and spank you,' Adam snapped. He semed unaware of how painfully his hands were biting into her shoulders, for he did not release her, even when she asked him, but held her, staring down into her flushed face. A burnished gold strand of hair was caught against her cheek. He brushed it away. His touch was as light as gossamer, yet even so she caught her breath.

'Let me go, please?' she entreated. He was looking at her so strangely, as though he had never really seen her properly before. Already her knees were growing weak, and it had nothing to do with the ride.

'I chased a petulant child, but I think I have caught a woman,' he murmured softly, gathering her into his arms.

She had no strength to resist him. Neither did she want to. This time she was willing—and eager—for his kiss. Her lips opened and flared to life beneath his. She could feel the fierce beating of his heart as he crushed her against him. He wanted her! He could not deny it. And he had been angry, not because he had been beaten but because she had been in danger. Natália's heart flooded with happiness.

Excitement rose inside her as he bent her back against the hard bark of a tree, moulding her body against his until she knew he could feel every curve of her. His lips spilled hot kisses down over her cheek and the smooth line of her throat, and returned to sear her mouth until a soft moan escaped her and she clung to him, the fire within her growing. Tomorrow or the next day he would leave her and go away. She would never see him again. She would marry Cesar and live in a comfortable house in Setúbal and learn somehow to be a wife and mother, but she would never forget these moments with Adam Sorrell, for now she knew what it was to be a woman! To experience a woman's deep passions. To know the bitter-sweet heartache of wanting a man she could not have.

CHAPTER THREE

'I KISSED YOU because you are a lovely young thing. It means nothing . . . nothing binding. I hope you understand that,' Adam said, and was surprised at the harshness of his voice. He had kissed countless women in his life, but never had one aroused the primitive man in him as this one did. Yet, to look at her now, he could hardly believe the depths of emotion he had felt in her soft lips, or in the soft, pliant body beneath his hands. She looked so calm, in total control of herself—and of the fire inside her.

They had walked the last few yards to the pleasant little *tasca* set in an olive grove, and now sat at a well-worn table with a bottle of wine between them. The young girl who had come out to serve them had stared in disbelief at Natália, then rushed inside to wash the glasses and bring a clean cloth to hide the peeling paint on the sun-baked wood. Adam was aware of curious faces peering through the window as he poured red wine for them both. She declined his offer of a piece of *chouriço*, a highly spiced sausage that was as popular with Portuguese people as their *caldo* or *aguardente*, and selected instead a thin slice of the Serra cheese he had produced from his saddlebag, and a large black olive.

She had brushed back the loose hair from her face and her cheeks, which, although containing a touch of colour, were nowhere as bright a red as when he had released her from his embrace. He had expected at the very least a slap or the sharp end of her tongue, but she said not one word of reproach, only began to smooth down her crumpled skirts. A smile had touched his mouth as he recalled the stockinged legs and the white petticoats about her thighs.

As she looked across the table at him, a slender eyebrow winged upwards. For the space of a heartbeat, he was sure a wicked light danced in those brilliantly blue eyes before she lowered her gaze.

'Are you so afraid of being tied to one woman, Major Sorrell?' It was now her turn to laugh at him. She had never felt so relaxed before in the company of a man. Only an hour ago she had been a frightened, timid creature in his company, now she felt at ease and was in no hurry to see her sister and Drew appear on the horizon. 'I promise you, I do not consider one kiss binding, either. I beg your pardon—two kisses! Does that at least make us . . . friends?'

Adam watched her sip her wine and wondered why he should feel even the slightest irritation at this more casual attitude? Could he have been wrong? Was she more worldly than he imagined, playing a game with him? He would have sworn her indignation and anger had been genuine, but then, although he had known many different women, he did not consider himself an expert on them. Any man who did that was a fool. On too many occasions he had seen fellow officers, soldiers beneath his command, receive bad news from home. A wife or girl-friend had deserted them . . . rumours of unfaithfulness . . . a child fathered by another, which was why he would never take a wife while he was serving his country.

He was glad he would not be around long enough to find out if Natália Lareira was as fickle as her fellow creatures, for already he had to admit, reluctantly, that she had got beneath his skin.

'To—friendship.' He drained his glass and replenished it with a nod of surprise. 'This is indeed a fine, full-bodied wine. I must tell my father when I see him again.'

'Will that be soon?'

'I hope to be with him in Lisboa by tomorrow night. The luxury of a hot bath and a good cigar . . . the fine claret in his cellar.' Adam gave a soft laugh, unaware of the disquiet his words caused. Leaving so soon! The girl who had served them earlier came out to enquire if they required more wine, and he nodded, voicing his appreciation of what he had already consumed. As she went away, he became aware of Natália's eyes fixed on him, and realised for the first time that she had not commented on his fluency in Portuguese.

'I think there is much I do not know about you, Major Sorrell,' she murmured. 'You speak my language as though you were born to it.'

'I was born in England, but I have lived here since the age of six, and was educated, apart from a few months at Cambridge, at the University of Coimbra. My father is a merchant banker in Lisboa, although he has other varied interests. In wine, for one. I hope to return to that part of the business as soon as the war is over, and run it until I find a *quinta* of my own.'

'Like this one?' She had been right, Natália mused: the speculative eye he had cast over her father's vines had not been out of casual interest. Why could she not marry a man like this, who loved the land and would be willing to stay at the Quinta das Raposeiras with her as his wife? Quickly she squashed such an absurd idea, appealing as it was.

'Somehow I cannot see you planting the vines. My father used to do it himself—do you know that?—when he was very young. Even now he supervises every one that goes into the ground.' He loved them more than his daughters!

'My grandfather was a sea-captain. There was a time when I thought I might follow in his footsteps, but not any more. They are not unalike, the sea and the land. The sailor constantly wages battle with the sea, a farmer with the land. The relationship is rather like that between a man and a woman, do you not agree?'

Natália blushed at the question, conscious of amber flecks mocking her from those bold eyes. What kind of answer was he expecting?

'I see no reason why a man and a woman should not live in perfect harmony, if they love each other,' she replied truthfully. 'I think you are somewhat of a cynic, Major.'

'True. My years of soldiering, short that they have been, have not reassured me to the faithfulness of women.'

'Perhaps the right one has not yet come into your life; but with such an attitude, you would not recognise her worth if it confronted you.'

'Indeed I shall, Natália . . .' He leaned across the table to her as if to impart some startling revelation—or was that her imagination? For an instant, he looked so serious as he gazed into her face . . . Then a shout came from behind, and he lifted his eyes and she watched his whole body relax and sink slowly back into the chair.

When Drew and Alída joined them, he had already called for more glasses and food for the new arrivals. Natália felt almost crushed by the weight of her disappointment. What had he been about to say? Had he seen something in her he liked—or desired? Why, oh why was she torturing herself with such a question? As she had said, two kisses were not binding on either of them. Yet for her, if not him, nothing would ever be the same again. Never would she forget Adam Sorrell.

'Natália? What are you doing here? Surely you are not alone?' Alída gave a disapproving frown as she sat close to her sister. What a handsome pair they made, had been her first impression as she came upon them. The dark good looks of the English officer, coupled with her sister's pale skin and hair of burnished gold.

'Of course not, she is with my brother.' Drew grinned

as he sampled the wine Adam poured for him. 'And quite safe! Father will love this. Can we take him a couple of dozen bottles?'

'My sentiments exactly. I will have a word with Dom Abílio before we leave.' Natália saw Adam's lips twitch with amusement at his brother's assumption that she was 'safe' with him. She felt the exact opposite!

'I am sure Father will be delighted to supply you with whatever you want from his warehouses in Lisboa,' Alída returned smilingly, as she managed to mask a certain uneasiness at Natália's casualness in the presence of Adam Sorrell. Had she not known better, she might have taken them for old friends. 'I can take you and Drew there if you wish.'

'Alída is accompanying us to the city. Father will be pleased to meet her.' Drew supplied the information reluctantly as his brother's eyes fixed on him quizzingly. He knew Adam's views on becoming seriously involved with a woman while fighting a war, but things had developed to such a stage between himself and Alída that nothing short of marriage would do. He loved her with a desperation he had never known before. Girls found him amusing because of his shyness, laughed at his timid attempts to make them interested in him . . . It had not been like that with Alída. From the first moment they had met in Mafra at a *festa*, they had become friends. Now they were more. Soon he would place a ring on her finger and make her his for ever.

'When Drew returns to headquarters, I shall open up my house in Mafra again,' Alída said, not looking at Natália. How could she condemn her sister for seeking a few moments of diversionary happiness when she was doing the very same? Although, for her, there was the security of marriage with the man she loved at the end of the road. For Natália, only marriage . . . and she knew very well the depths of misery to which a woman could sink when she was matched with a man she did not

love—and even feared. Instinctively she knew that
Natália had not mentioned Cesar to her companion.

The house in Mafra had been Alída's refuge after the
death of her husband. She had never liked it when he
was alive, but once she became a widow, she developed
her own circle of friends, unhampered by her husband's
demands that she seek out only influential people, army
officers who might be able to further his career. Had any
one of them showed the slightest interest in her that he
was aware of—some had, but she had managed to hide
the fact from him—she had no doubt he would have
thrust her into bed with him without a second thought!
She shuddered slightly, and became aware of Adam's
searching gaze on her. He doesn't like me, she thought.
He is afraid I shall take his brother away from him. As I
am afraid he will steal the heart of my romantic little
sister. If he has not done so already!

Natália was looking at her now, almost pleadingly,
and Alída knew she was waiting for an invitation to
accompany her to Lisboa as an escape from the multi-
tude of wedding preparations that would begin once
Cesar returned to Alto Verde—and that would be any
day now. Often they had stayed in the city together and
enjoyed not only each other's company, as they had
done since childhood, but the sense of freedom that
always prevailed for them once they were out of their
father's scrutiny. Those days were over for poor Natália,
and her sister's heart went out to her in the last desperate
days of her freedom.

Even so, she did not want her to do anything foolish
—such as thinking Adam Sorrell was anything like his
brother. From what Drew had said—even though she
knew he cared for his brother deeply—he was a hardened soldier who took his pleasures where he found
them and had no intention of settling down. He was too
handsome, too sure of himself, she reasoned. He could
turn the head of any gullible girl, and there was not one

more gullible and fanciful than Natália with her head full of dreams.

'When—when are you leaving?" Natália asked, when the answer to her silent question was not forthcoming.

'The day after tomorrow. We are staying for the *festa*, of course.' Alída's choice of going with Drew, or remaining to give her sister moral support as her wedding day loomed closer, had been a difficult one. She had put her own happiness first, and hoped that Natália would understand.

'I had hoped to start out tomorrow,' Adam said with a quick frown, and his words heightened Natália's growing disappointment. Was everyone deserting her? 'What shall we be missing?'

'Dia das Flores,' Alída told him. 'There will be no work for anyone in the village. There will be dancing in the streets, lots of eating and drinking . . . and a wedding in the evening. Paulo Santos, the youngest son of the miller, is being married to Maria Heléna Lurdes. Her father is the blacksmith. Father is providing the wedding feast.'

'I see no harm in the men remaining for one more day,' Drew murmured with a grin. 'Relax, brother. Let's enjoy life while we can.'

'I intend to—in Lisboa,' Adam returned drily, but after a moment he nodded. 'Why not? They deserve whatever pleasures they can find before they are plunged back into the thick of it all.'

'It will be fun,' Alída cried, clapping her hands in excitement.

'For those who have an escort, perhaps,' Natália remarked quietly. 'I don't relish the thought of dancing with Dona Margarida all night . . . or with Father; he always treads on my toes and calls me clumsy.' She looked at Adam and smiled. At that smile Alída caught her breath so sharply that Drew's hand covered hers, as if he, too, sensed something he did not quite understand between the two people opposite. 'Unless, of course, the gallant Major will take pity on me and be my escort?'

For an instant a strange gleam flickered in Adam's tawny eyes, then a smile twitched at the corners of the lean mouth at her audacity. He nodded, and said casually, almost with indifference,

'Why not?' Across the table Drew chuckled, but he ignored it.

As he was helping Natália to mount for the return ride to the house, however, she found herself held firmly in his grasp. His face only a few inches from hers was impassive. His voice, too quiet to carry to Drew and Alída, momentarily chilled her with its coldness.

'If there is any asking to be done, *menina*, I shall do it. Remember that. I am a man who makes up his own mind.'

'Have you taken leave of your senses?' Alída enquired, flinging down her gloves and coat. She had followed Natália to her room, determined to warn her of the consequences of her foolish act. 'Whatever possessed you to ask him outright to escort you? What if Father finds out?'

'Will you tell him? No, of course not. Nor would I reveal your liaison with Drew Sorrell. You are more than friends, Alída, I know it, and I suspect you have no intention of telling him you are to be married,' Natália flung back. She was slumped in a chair, while Pilar pulled off her riding boots and fetched her a change of clothes. She felt elated by what she had done. 'I shall have him for another day! Don't you understand?'

'Natália, what have you done?' Her sister sank on to the bed. Neither of them was aware of Pilar listening intently as she slipped Natália's feet into warm slippers and then began to pick up discarded clothes. 'He—he has not—made love to you?'

'No! Nor tried,' came the indignant answer. Had she not broken away from that first embrace, would he have continued, she wondered? Would she have allowed further boldness? Never! It was not as if she loved him . . . Love? It was the first time she had considered how deep her feelings were for the Englishman. He had taken her by storm, giving her no chance to think, to analyse her thoughts or emotions . . . 'He is a gentleman, but . . .'

'What is it? You look so strange?' Alída whispered, somewhat alarmed at her sister's wide-eyed expression.

'Could . . .?' No. It was impossible! But she had never known such excitement at a man's touch. She knew nothing of love, so how would she recognise it? 'He —he has kissed me,' she admitted, as if divulging a life-or-death secret. 'And I liked it. Why shouldn't I?'

'And you think a kiss will twist him round your finger? Oh, Natália, he is not Cesar! Pompous, conceited, selecting a wife as he would a new statue for his house. This is a man! And you are a . . .'

'. . . child? Not any more,' Natália said softly, almost dreamily. 'Something has happened to me, I feel it here . . .' She touched a hand to her heart. 'I want to be with him, hear his voice, have him hold me, kiss me. He is everything I have ever dreamed of in a man.'

'Major Sorrell is not a dream, he is reality. A very dangerous reality, I fear.' Alída came to her side and sat on the arm of the chair, slipping an arm tightly about her shoulders. 'I am worried for you. How can I not be? I have never seen you look at anyone the way you looked at him today. If Father finds out you were alone with him . . .'

'But we all went riding together, did we not?'

'Yes. Yes, that will be the best story . . . if you were seen.'

How could she not have been seen as she rode with Adam in hot pursuit through the countryside, Natália wondered, but wisely she did not mention the incident.

'You do not think of me as a child any longer, do you?' she pleaded, desperate for just one person to side with her.

'Not only a child, but a stupid one if you play games with that man!'

'I only want what you have—with Drew,' Natália said solemnly. 'Is that too much to ask?'

'You are betrothed to Cesar. He could return at any time. If he hears talk . . . I do not want you to experience the kind of unhappy marriage I did, dearest little Natália. You must make your own happiness. Accept him as your husband. Do the best you can.'

'For one day—tomorrow—I shall make my own happiness, and then Adam Sorrell will be gone from my life. After that, I don't care what happens to me. No man will ever make me feel as he does!' Bright tears glistened in Natália's eyes. She turned and buried her face against her sister's shoulder with a cry which tore at the heart of the maid by the door. 'I think I love him!'

On every narrow, twisting cobbled alley there were lights in the windows of the small huddled-together houses, and doors were thrown open wide. People outside greeted those within as they passed. Chairs were brought into the open for those—especially the older inhabitants, who just wanted to sit and listen to the music—to watch the candlelit procession passing below and tell how it had been in their day. Leathered faces of men and women alike wrinkled with pleasure as young children rushed past with grotesque masks on their faces, their voices raised with shrill excitement, or a relative appeared bringing food and wine. For today no one, young or old, was forgotten in Alto Verde. Long-standing grievances were put aside, friendships renewed. It was a time of being together, and remembering, . . . of hoping . . . planning . . . All the prayers were that soon the French would leave the soil of Portugal and set them free to go back to the old ways . . . to the land, which was all most of them knew and had ever known, and all their children would know for generations to come. It was a good life!

Enthusiasm followed the procession, which wound its way through the village, led by baby-faced Tomaz, carrying an image of the Virgin Mary—how many smiled as they watched him, remembering how only the day before his mother had taken a stick to him for stealing precious apples from her storeroom—followed by the priest, Father José, in his black robes, his white hair and beard shining in the light of the candles surrounding him. The youngest member of Alto Verde, only a week old, was carried in the arms of a proud mother.

And there was Daniel, at ninety, garlanded with flowers, a giggling girl on each arm. Born in Alto Verde, he had never put one foot outside it. No chair for him. No pipe or *aguardente* to dull his brain. At least, not yet! He wanted laughter, to know again the joy of life, which at times like these was made especially pleasurable by the pretty young girls who helped him on his way, kissed a brown cheek and told him how young he looked. Now that was living! *Graças a Deus!*

The early part of the day had been spent in a whirlwind of last-minute preparations. Paper streamers hung from the trees, and festooned windows and balconies of some of the taller houses. Coloured lanterns, carefully preserved over the years, illuminated dark side-roads, where flower-strewn archways awaited the arrival of the procession that would slowly, painstakingly, wend its way down each of them in turn.

Many people carried flowers, from a single bloom to carefully prepared bouquets, wherever they went. Back-breaking hours of labour had produced cart after cart of floral arrangements in all shapes and sizes. There were clowns, devils with huge horns, and the crowning glory—a bower of wild passion-flowers where the queen of Dia das Flores, Maria Heléna Lurdes, would rest as she was carried to the church for her wedding. Not as many exhibits as in the days before the French came, but what did it matter? Not even they could stop such occasions up and down the country. They did not understand—these soldiers who came to steal and plunder, to take what did not belong to them wherever they went—that so long as people could be close at such times, come together and remember how it had once been, pray for the day it would be so again . . . and still be patient and enjoy whatever mode of life existed for them at this moment, that they could never win. They could never break the mighty spirit which prevailed among the people.

From the window of her bedroom, Natália watched the sky grow dark and the first candles flicker and glow. Without hesitation she lighted the one Pilar placed in front of her, and set it on a table before the french windows. There was great activity from the direction of the barn where the *guerrilleros* were staying, but she could see no sign of Adam Sorrell. She waited, feeling her heart begin to pound more quickly, but he did not appear, and reluctantly she turned away. *Patiência*. In a little while, she would have him all to herself for a whole evening.

Pilar draped a black woollen shawl about her mistress's shoulders and stood back admiringly. Natália wore a voluminous skirt of fine black cloth, trimmed about the bottom with alternate wide and narrow bands of black velvet ribbon. The apron about her waist, also of cloth, was bright red, and edged with *passementerie*. A tight-fitting black jacket reached to her hips, edged in gold lace, with the sleeves slashed from elbow to wrist to reveal the snow-white undersleeves of her chemisette. About her neck she wore her mother's large gold cross on a heavy chain, together with several more plain linked chains. For the occasion Pilar had provided a necklace of coins—gold, Natália suspected—but where the woman had acquired such a fortune in jewellery, she dared not ask. Her stockings were white, her shoes of black leather adorned with small red ribbon rosettes.

The abundance of thick hair was plaited and tied with velvet to match the bows, and hung in a single plait down her back, reaching to her waist. On her head, a froth of white lace which cascaded each side of cheeks flushed with excitement. Her features were obscured by a black cloth mask, trimmed with gold. She had every intention of taking the fullest advantage of the opportunities the *festa* offered.

Usually she did not bother to hide her face. Everyone in Alto Verde was too afraid of Cesar, who usually escorted her on such occasions, to invite her to join in the merrymaking, and she had to be content with watching from the sidelines, infrequently being asked to dance . . . but only by her father or her betrothed. Tonight would be different! There was no Cesar to scrutinise her every move, and she hoped her father would be too busy with the forthcoming wedding breakfast to watch over her too closely. She had deliberately chosen the local costume, which would allow her to blend among the other village women. Tonight was hers! No one was going to take it from her!

Alída came into the room, and Natália gave a cry of admiration at her pale green muslin gown over a deeper green satin undershift. She wore a cluster of artificial flowers in her short hair, and another at her bosom, where the neckline of her gown dipped daringly low. Never before had she seen her sister look so radiant. At last she had discarded the dismal mourning clothes.

'If Drew Sorrell is not already in love with you, he will be after one look at you tonight. Alída, you . . . you sparkle, do you know that?'

'I wish I did not feel so happy, when I am about to spoil your own happiness and the evening you have planned for yourself,' Alída said, her voice hushed. 'Natália—dear Natália—Cesar has returned! He is downstairs with Father now, and I have been sent to fetch you. He intends to escort you himself this evening. You will have no chance, no chance at all, to be with Adam. My dear, I am so sorry.'

Natália stood stock still, her mind refusing to accept this unexpected shock which spelled ruin to the blissful hours she had envisaged in the company of Adam Sorrell. It could not be!

'No!' The single word torn from her lips made Alída wince with pain. How cruel fate was not to have allowed her a few stolen hours . . . Yet, perhaps it was for the better. In Cesar's company, she would have to forget that the handsome Englishman existed, for she would not be allowed to leave his side. Cesar's jealousy did not stem from love, or any feeling of affection for the girl he was soon to marry, but from a possessive mania that made her life a misery whenever they were together.

'I am so sorry,' Alída repeated, knowing how hollow the words sounded. Natália needed more than words, but she had nothing to give her. It was over for her sister. The brief interlude of dreaming. Over. 'Are you all right?'

Natália lifted her shoulders in an abject shrug of acceptance.

'*Sim.* I shall come down directly. Don't wait for me. There is no reason why the evening should be ruined for you, too. Go on, I'm all right. I promise.'

Cesar João Ferreira Duarte was a man of medium height, already showing signs of thickening round the waist and in his dark face. In his youth he had been somewhat of a ladies' man, keeping as many as three mistresses in three different towns and distributing his time between them throughout the year . . . much to the chagrin of his parents, whose demise had been hastened by his complete lack of morals. It was, of course, permissible to have a mistress, what man did not, perhaps two? But three . . . who wrenched him away from his estates and demanded his undivided attention! In the end everyone suffered, most of all Cesar. His indulgences cost him parents, home, almost every escudo he possessed, and it had taken more than ten years to recoup his losses. Parents could not be replaced, but he had cared little about them, never having been on the best of terms with an over-doting mother and a father who expected too much of his pleasure-loving son.

He had managed to purchase back the house and lands he had been forced to sell in order to maintain his orgies of wild living, and was now frugal to the point of meanness. He still had a mistress, but only one, and soon he would have a wife, to run his home. The other could be discarded and replaced, but his wife would remain, to care for his needs and his house. He had chosen Natália because of her youth, her innocence and the large dowry which accompanied her. When Abílio Lareira died, she would inherit a half share in the *quinta*, as he had no male heir. With the other sister a widow who was showing no signs of remarrying, despite her father's insistence that she do so, there was a chance that Natália might produce a son. Then he knew, without a doubt, that the *quinta* would be left entirely to him. It was Cesar's intention to make sure that it was.

He did not care about her one way or the other: she was a means to an end. He would continue with his mistresses until the day he died, taking them, discarding them when they became too clinging or greedy . . . Never again would he ruin himself over a woman . . . But Natália would always be there when he wanted her. And he did want her. Her constant aloofness from his advances annoyed him. He found pleasure in the thought of moulding her to his ways once they were married. Then, she would refuse him nothing!

He turned to watch her come into the room. She wore a bright yellow gown, caught high beneath the bosom with a jewelled brooch. Her hair was wound into a tight plait on the crown of her head. His eyes fastened almost hungrily on the firm swell of her breasts above the revealing *décolletage*, and his mouth grew dry at the thought of possessing her. To his surprise, she met his bold gaze without flinching and extended her hand for him to kiss. Despite her apparent calmness, however, he felt a tremor run through the fingers he touched to his lips. He knew she hated his touch. Let her. Soon there would be nothing she could do about it. Soon she would be his wife . . . soon the mother of a fine son, as many as he could father, and he would be master of the Quinta das Raposeiras when the old man died.

'Natália, my dear, how charming you look. You must stay close to me tonight or I shall have you stolen away by some adventurous young man.' He chuckled, but there was no humour in the hard eyes which met hers. It was a warning that she belonged to him, and that he would not tolerate another man looking at her—let alone touching her.

'I would not share your affections with another', Adam had told her as they stood together in the vineyard. 'Not even a single smile, however innocent.' When he looked at her, she wanted no other man. She would revel in *his* jealousy . . . but Cesar . . . Somehow she managed to smile as she withdrew her hand. He always held it longer than was necessary; it was only one of his many ways of asserting his authority over her and of showing her he could touch her whenever he pleased and that she could do nothing about it. The thought of marriage to him was now twice as distasteful as it had been before the Englishman rode into Alto Verde. She wondered how he would react if he learned that the gown she wore was not for his benefit, but that of Adam Sorrell, so that the Englishman would recognise her, even masked!

'I am sure no man would be foolish enough to flirt with me while you are my escort,' Natália returned quietly.

Save one, perhaps. To avoid Cesar's suspicions being aroused, she had sent Pilar to convey to Adam her profound apologies. The maid was to say that an old friend of her father had just arrived, and she was required to partner him for the early part of the evening. She would meet Adam, if he still wished it, at the church for the wedding of Maria Heléna.

She dared not trust Alída with the message, acutely aware of how remiss she had been in not openly explaining her situation at the beginning. Should Adam now learn that she was betrothed, he might think her conduct left a great deal to be desired, that she was only amusing herself with him while the man she was to marry was away. Uppermost in her mind, this evening, was to keep the news from him, lest it spoil the few short hours she could salvage.

As she sat miserably on the edge of the bed, Pilar had leaned over and whispered in her ear a plan so simple, yet daring, that Natália had immediately felt her heart soar with renewed hope, and without hesitation she grasped the offered straw.

That was why she was able to bear Cesar's hand on hers, the touch of moist, hot lips on her bare skin. She would do nothing and say nothing to provoke his ire and cause him to watch her more closely than usual. With any luck, one of the village girls would distract him, enabling Natália to slip away.

'I think your return has brought a sparkle to my daughter's eyes,' Abílio declared as he watched them together. Natália felt herself grow hot beneath his scrutiny. He was looking at her so strangely. Had someone whispered in his ear about her wild ride with Adam? No, he would have rebuked her before this had the slightest hint of it reached him.

She was unaware how her eyes did indeed shine, with a brilliance that Abílio rarely saw. There was a flush to her pale cheeks which highlighted the fine bone structure inherited from her mother. He inwardly winced as he recalled his beautiful dead wife and the legacy she had bequeathed to him of two useless daughters. He knew at times he was uncommonly strict with them both, but it was in their best interests. Natália in particular had been singled out for special care and attention. At all costs he had to ensure that the wildness in her was tamed before she grew much older. Cesar would succeed where he himself had failed over the years. He was not the best of men to have chosen as her husband, but he had the same wish as Abílio himself had—for a family. Both men desired their names to be borne by future generations. If only he could find the words to tell Natália how fortunate she was to have a wealthy husband, of good background, despite the misdemeanours of his youth, who would give her security for the rest of her life. He could not, however. When he tried to analyse his feelings, he came to the reluctant conclusion that he would have liked to grow closer to both his daughters, but that would have meant sharing with them the love he had shared with their mother—and that was impossible, for it had all died with her.

Somehow Natália endured the hours which followed in Cesar's company, with a fixed smile on her face, and a growing fear in her heart that Adam Sorrell cared little whether or not she met him later on. Whenever she saw him he was dancing with a pretty girl, or drinking with his men. He had acknowledged her and the two men with her when she first came out of the house, but after that he was careful not to look her way. Alída and Drew were never more than a few inches from each other throughout the evening. She became aware of the growing frown on her father's face as he found them always together, dancing, or standing close as they watched others enjoying themselves. She suspected that Alída had not informed him of her impending departure for Lisboa. How lonely and miserable she would be when her sister went!

She heard Cesar mutter under his breath, and found that his attention was focused on Adam, who was dancing most energetically with yet another of the village girls. 'The British are growing as free with our women as the French were,' he muttered, and although the words were spoken quietly, they were uttered as the man in question happened to pass close by. From the momentary stiffening of his back, Natália knew he had heard.

A pair of cold eyes focused on Cesar as he interrupted a step to wheel about, seeking the man who had uttered the insult. Without a word he allowed his gaze to wander slowly up and down Cesar's immaculately clad form, lingering on the thickening waist and the face glowing from an excess of rich red wine. In that single look was contempt conveyed more eloquently than in a thousand words, and when he turned away and continued to partner the young girl at his side, Cesar's ruddy complexion was the colour of a beetroot.

'The insolent young puppy! I'll have him up in front of his commanding officer,' he blustered, conscious of the smirks and veiled delight in the eyes of many of the Alto Verde villagers.

'I doubt that very much,' Abílio answered. 'From what I hear of Major Sorrell, he has friends in high places. Your remark was uncalled for, Cesar. The Major and his brother . . . and his men'—heavy emphasis was laid on the last words, leaving Cesar in no doubt that his words had been a mistake—'are guests in Alto Verde. *My* guests. Please be kind enough to remember that.'

Natália could hardly believe her ears. Was this really

her father being so authoritative? He tolerated the foreign soldiers who passed through the village, but never before had she known him to defend them against Cesar's malicious remarks. She wanted to smile at him and convey her thanks, but knew that to do so might cause him to wonder what interest *she* had in Adam Sorrell, and so she remained with her eyes downcast.

A pair of highly polished boots appeared in her vision. She heard Cesar utter an oath, and his fingers fastened about her wrist so tightly that she gave an involuntary cry of pain. Not daring to believe Adam's boldness, she lifted her eyes and encountered his quizzical smile.

'Senhorita Lareira, as I am leaving soon, will you take pity on a poor soldier and permit me one dance?'

'She will not! You impertinent . . . !' The murderous look directed at him froze the words in Cesar's throat.

'I don't know who you are, senhor, but I am a guest here. I shall not abuse the hospitality of my gracious host by calling you out. However, should we ever meet outside Alto Verde, it will give me a great pleasure to accommodate you! I detest loud-mouthed men who do not have the courage to wear a uniform, and look down their noses at braver men . . . at strangers who are prepared to sacrifice their lives far from their own homes.'

'Major Sorrell, I think you have said enough,' Abílio intervened, growing perturbed at the anger he could hear in the younger man's voice. Cesar deserved it and more for his stupidity, but he wanted no ill-feeling on this day. He could not help regretting, however, that he had been unable to find a son-in-law with a backbone to match that of Adam Sorrell. A man who spoke his mind and shamed the devil! And was prepared to back it up with pistol or sword. That was the kind of man Natália should have had. With such strength surrounding her, she might have found true happiness. And what children such a union would have produced! He shook his head slightly to rid his mind of such thoughts. It was too late for regrets. The die had been cast.

'Forgive me. Senhorita Lareira . . .' He was holding out his arm to Natália. He did not expect a refusal to his invitation.

Disengaging herself from Cesar's grasp, she picked up her skirts and laid a hand lightly on the offered arm. She did not look at Cesar or her father as he led her away, and did not breathe easily until they were in the midst of the square and surrounded by grinning faces.

'You were most unwise to provoke Cesar,' she said in a low urgent tone. 'He is an excellent shot. He has killed men for less than you said to him!'

'Has he now? A pity his energies are not directed towards the French, then. Or does he have a yellow streak down his back?' Adam flung at her with heavy sarcasm. There was a possessiveness in the way Cesar acted that disturbed him.

'He is no coward . . . At least, I don't think so. He does not choose to fight, that's all. He has an estate to look after, and people who depend on him. Like father has. You would not expect him to go off and fight at his age, would you? Alída and I could not run the *quinta* by ourselves. Much of the food we produce here, not to mention the wine, is consumed by your soldiers, remember.'

'Such concern for an old friend of your father,' Adam teased, and her cheeks flamed. 'Do you care about that barrel of lard? He is a close friend of yours also, perhaps?'

'Cesar is one of father's closest—and oldest—friends, and I have known him since I was a little girl. Please, Adão . . .' She used the Portuguese equivalent of Adam's name without realising it, as her anxiety grew that a quarrel might somehow develop between the two men. The insults which had passed between them would not be forgotten by either man, she realised. 'The wine makes him . . . disagreeable. It will pass. Stay away from him for the remainder of the evening.'

'If I do, where will you be?' For a moment, as they came together in the dance, Adam's fingers lingered on the red marks still visible on her soft skin where Cesar had held her.

'Did Pilar not tell you? I shall join you at the church. By then Cesar will have drunk more wine, and it will be time for Father to give the bride away.'

'And when he sees us together, he will approve?'

'He will not know who is with you,' Natália returned, with a secretive smile that caused his eyebrows to rise, but she had no intention of enlightening him. 'Take me back now. I shall join you at the church.'

CHAPTER FOUR

THE LITTLE village church was crammed full of people. Children, bored with standing still for too long, ran about outside, or played hide-and-seek among the low branches of the fig trees, but inside it was very quiet. All eyes were focused on the couple being married. Handkerchiefs dabbed at moist eyes as memories of other wedding days returned. Adam stood at the back of the gathering, by the open door. His brother and Alída stood side by side a little way in front of him. He found himself watching them, frowning at the silent intimacy which prevailed between them. He wondered if they were even aware of people pressing in on them from all sides.

He saw Drew slip his arm round the girl's shoulders as the ceremony drew to a close, and she laid her head against his shoulder with a shy smile. The young fool had got himself well and truly hooked this time! This one had marriage on her mind. After debating whether he should try to dissuade her from accompanying them to Lisboa, he decided it was none of his business. If Drew was old enough to get his head blown off, he was old enough to make a fool of himself with a woman. Maybe the whole thing would peter out once they had spent more time together. He was exceedingly fond of his brother and did not want to see him hurt by some flighty widow who would forget him as soon as he had returned to the war.

Adam looked about him, casting an eye over the men and women pressing close behind him, but could see no sign of a bright yellow dress to herald Natália's arrival. Perhaps she had been delayed, or prevented from coming at all. He was well aware of the code of conduct which ruled all Portuguese homes, and was surprised that she had even suggested meeting him alone and unchaperoned. Was she so trusting? Or, once out of sight of a duenna and her father, was she prepared to accommodate his needs? How many soldiers had . . . ? Roughly he quashed such a notion. She was no woman of easy virtue—he would stake his life on it— nevertheless, the thought that she might not meet him left him with a sense of frustration. He should have been pleased that the short but tempestuous relationship was curtailed before either of them became too involved in something neither could finish at this time, but he was not. He wanted to see her again, to look into those expressive sapphire eyes and convince himself that one day he would come back to Alto Verde.

As the crowd parted to allow the newly married couple through, he slipped outside into the warm night air. Discarding his jacket, he draped it over one shoulder and leaned against a wall to light a *cigarrillo*. Laughing, chattering women rushed past him, strewing the path of the bridal couple with flowers. The moment they appeared, they were lifted shoulder high to be carried to the waiting cart and deposited in the bower of sweet-smelling flowers for the short journey back to the square and the wedding feast.

And what a feast, he thought. When he had wandered past the tables, they were already being replenished with food and more *garrafas* of wine. Over open pits filled with grey ashes several suckling-pigs were being roasted, also chickens and a young lamb. The village might go short of meat in the months ahead, but tonight everyone would eat their fill and drink until it came out of their ears. Tomorrow there would be full stomachs—and aching heads—and the women would gather at the washing-place to scrub the clothes and discuss the evening. It would be a topic of conversation for many, many weeks.

He caught the faint aroma of perfume, and half turned as he felt a touch upon his arm. At the sight of the masked girl at his side, dressed in the traditional black skirt and white blouse, he suppressed the disappointment which once again rose inside him at the realisation that Natália would not be coming. She had sent her maid again, with another apology.

'Do they not make a perfect pair?' Natália murmured wistfully, and laughed softly as his eyes narrowed in disbelief. 'I said I would come, Major. Did you not believe me?'

'I was looking for a yellow dress and a bevy of sour-faced duennas prepared to guard your honour,' Adam returned drily, and found that he had openly admitted he had been looking for her. Did it please her? he wondered. Behind the decorated mask, it was difficult to see her eyes clearly.

'Dona Margarida will be in the house snoring her head off by now. Tonight my honour is in your hands. The hands of an English officer and a gentleman,' she added quickly, as if to remind him she was not to be taken for granted.

'Your wish is my command.' If she were discovered with him, there would be the very devil to pay, Adam reflected as they followed in the wake of the wedding party, even though she was perfectly safe with him. 'What do you want to do?'

'Dance, join in the fun like everyone else. Like Alída and your brother. Is it too much to ask? Always I must remember I am a lady, the daughter of Senhor Abílio Armandio Maria Lareira. I must conduct myself at all times like . . . like a nun.' And that is what she would become if this little escapade leaked out, Natália thought with a momentary shiver of apprehension. For Cesar to find her with another man, only weeks before their marriage . . . He would disown her, abandon her to her father's wrath, of that she was sure. She would be forced to retire to a convent to spend the rest of her days contemplating her foolishness. 'Why is it so wrong to want to enjoy myself?'

'I should say that entirely depends on how you intend to go about it,' came the amused reply, as Adam tucked her hand beneath his arm, guiding her over the uneven cobbles of a narrow alley. Someone ducked in front of them, peered into Natália's masked features, laughed, and thrust a bottle of wine into Adam's hand.

'Enjoy yourself, *amigo!*'

Natália gave a nervous laugh and pressed closer to him. Suddenly she did not feel so secure in her disguise. Before she had changed clothes with Pilar, she had told her father she had been seized with a sudden, unpleasant headache and would go to rest in her room until it subsided. Cesar had escorted her ungraciously to the door, which had been closed firmly in his face, and locked. Angrily he had stormed out of the house again, and from her window Natália had seen him begin drinking heavily. Ten minutes later, she had left Pilar and hurried down a back staircase and out into the throng of people milling about the house. It had all been so simple. Now here she was with Adam, her hand held tightly in his . . . and she was afraid. Afraid of being discovered, or of committing herself to this act of folly? How forward he must think her! A bold hussy. Doubtless he had encountered many women willing to grant favours to a lonely soldier. Was he lonely, she wondered, looking up into the dark face. He had opened the bottle, easing the cork from the neck with strong white teeth, and she watched the wine flow down his throat. She shook her head when it was offered to her, then, with reckless desperation, grasped it and allowed him to trickle a little between her lips.

'I—I was thirsty,' she said quickly, as a gleam came into his eyes. 'Cesar never stops talking.'

'About himself, I expect.'

'Mostly. Major Sorrell, I don't want you to mis-understand . . .'

'Your desire to kick over the traces and get a little fun out of life before you are hemmed in by marriage and surrounded by a family of wailing infants?' Adam inter-posed, and she was glad of the shadows which hid her embarrassment from him. 'I see nothing wrong in steal-ing a few hours to do what you want. We shall do exactly as you want—and nothing more. We shall dance and eat, and when we are hot and dry, we shall rest under the trees and enjoy some wine. We shall talk of nothing that displeases you.'

'You—you are very understanding. Thank you.'

The glance he threw her had more than a hint of ironic amusement in it. Some time later, foot-weary and breathless, he commandeered another bottle of wine, helped himself to a pile of chicken legs from one of the tables, and led her away from the noise and music to the peace of a small orange orchard. He laid his jacket on the ground for her and she sank on to it with a sigh.

'I haven't danced so much since Alída was married.'

'Was it an occasion for celebrating, then? From what Drew has told me, I rather gained the impression the marriage was not a happy one.'

'It wasn't. Her husband was a brute,' Natália replied, biting into the tender flesh of one of the chicken legs. 'Alída was afraid of him. I didn't like him much, either. That night—her wedding night—we both danced until we were exhausted . . . for different reasons. We are close, you see. I could hardly bear the thought of her leaving home, and going away with a stranger. How different it is for Maria Hélena! She has loved Paulo since she was twelve years old. They will be very happy and have lots of children.'

'God forbid!' said Adam. 'The child is barely sixteen, I'd say. What kind of a life will she have, saddled with youngsters at that age? She hasn't had time to discover life, and already she has thrown it away.'

'That isn't fair,' Natália protested, shocked by his words. 'She loves him. That is everything.'

'And what do you know of love, little fledgling? Why is it that women like weddings so much?' He found it hard to keep the laughter from his voice.

'Why is it that men run away from them?' she flung back, stung by his criticism. 'It is obvious that you are not married.'

'Nor do I intend to be for a long, long time. I intend to live my life to the full before I settle down.'

'If the French do not put a bullet in you first.'

'There is always that possibility,' Adam answered bleakly.

She gave a contrite little cry and leaned towards him, laying a hand on his arm. Beneath her fingers she could feel his muscles, stiff with anger. Anger or pain? 'I spoke thoughtlessly. Please forgive me?'

His fingers curled about hers. Slowly he drew her against his chest. She was aware of the heavy sweet smell of wine on his breath as he kissed her, as she allowed her lips to part and answer him. Her head swam. It could not be too much of her father's wine, for she had hardly drunk any. It was him!

'You are forgiven,' Adam murmured, easing his mouth from hers. He was annoyed by the tremor in his tone. Her breasts were pressing hard against the silk of his shirt. He could hear the beating of her heart . . . like that of a little bird. His fingers reached for her shoulder, then fell away. He was unaware of the disappointment that crossed her face beneath the mask. He only knew that to linger further might provoke the very situation between them he sought to avoid. So long as they stayed with people, they were safe . . . he was safe. Alone with her, to feel the softness of her so invitingly against him, would spell disaster for his resolves of will-power. No woman had ever affected him with such devastating emotions, shattering the shield which had sustained his bachelorhood for so long. Natália Lareira, wittingly or unwittingly, had reached him.

Sensing an inner disquiet in him, Natália drew away. There was an expression on his features she could not comprehend, and it disturbed her.

'Perhaps we should go back and dance,' she faltered. It was not what she wanted, but it was safer. In his arms, she had no mind of her own. She wanted him to make love to her, and was swept with a feeling of shame that her duenna's lectures and her father's stern lessons would avail her naught if he attempted to do so. She loved him. She was sure of it, now, and of the emotions which could run riot over sensible reasoning. When he touched her, she did not want to be sensible. She wanted to know love before it was too late! She would run away! That was the answer. Alída would give her shelter in Mafra, and hide her until Adam returned from the fighting.

'Yes, I believe that would be a good idea.' Adam rose, and lifted her to her feet. She was aware how carefully he did so, stepping back from her the moment she was upright. No, she would not go to Mafra. He did not want her. She was just another girl to amuse him until he returned to his duties. In silence she turned away and began to walk back to the square. Picking up his jacket, he followed. She did not hear the string of oaths that broke beneath his breath.

Too late Pilar realised that Cesar had seen her slip out of the house. She had patiently waited in the bedroom with the door securely locked, should he attempt to gain an entry, until she was sure he would have been diverted. He was easily distracted by a pretty face, especially when he had been drinking. She knew of several girls from the village who had shared his bed since he had come to stay at the *quinta*. He paid them handsomely to remain silent about his indescretions, but there was little Pilar did not know of the goings-on in the house. She made it her business to know. Anything that affected Natália affected her, too. She had racked her brains as the day of the wedding approached, trying to find a way her mistress could rid herself of this unwanted menace in her life. Short of slipping a dagger between his shoulder blades while he slept, she had found no solution. The knife was a last, desperate resort. If he ever hurt Natália, or brought her one moment of pain or grief when she was his wife, Pilar would not hesitate.

She paused out in the courtyard, heard a door slam somewhere behind her, and was on the point of turning when Cesar's arm went about her waist, lifting her bodily from the ground and bearing her back into the darkness. His hot mouth sought hers. His hands searched her body in the crudest fashion.

'Natália . . . lovely little Natália. It's only me.' He was quite drunk, she realised, scarcely able to pronounce his words clearly. She tried to struggle, but he had her arms pinned to her side. When she opened her mouth to shout for help, he thrust his free hand over it. She panicked as he used the full weight of his body to push her down to the ground. He had dragged her into the stables, and the near-by horses snorted in apprehension at the new arrivals.

'You were willing to give time to the English officer, so now you can spend some with me! Did you think I really believed you had a headache? It's time I showed you how much I want you, little Natália. After tonight, you will have no reason to run away from me.'

Pilar shuddered as he fastened his fingers in the front of her bodice and ripped it open. She still had not spoken a word. And in that moment she knew exactly how she could free her innocent mistress from the lust of this drunken animal. He was too drunk to realise he had the wrong woman . . . She turned her face away to avoid his hot breath, and was still . . .

Although it was after midnight, the revelry had not diminished. In fact, as the wine flowed like a swollen river from the five-litre kegs, the bride and groom wisely departed to the cottage which had been given to them by Dom Abílio, leaving most of their guests none the wiser. Daniel, with the willing assistance of two different girls, led a procession of dancers through the dimly lighted streets and alleys. Only half of those who started out returned to replenish their thirst at the tables. Courting couples had slipped away in the darkness, exhausted children crawled into a corner to eat the honey cakes they had crammed into their pockets when no one was looking, Father José stopped to help a fragile, very unsteady parishioner to find his front door.

Drew and Alída were among those missing, Natália noticed. Adam was aware of it too, she realised, seeing his gaze sweep the darkened alleys.

'Do you disapprove?' she asked softly, and he gave a shrug, meant to indicate that he did not. But she suspected otherwise. He cared for his brother as deeply as she did for Alída. They wanted neither to be hurt. 'My sister deserves to be happy. If Drew does this for her, then I am glad for them both.'

'So am I, so long as . . .' He broke off, leaving the sentence unfinished.

'. . . she does not hurt him? Alída will not do that. Have you seen the way they look at each other? I envy what they have found.'

'Do you?' Adam turned and looked down at her, his eyes narrowing as he heard the sincerity in her voice. 'Drew is a fool if he expects any woman to wait for him while he goes off to fight. He doesn't have that right.'

'I don't agree with you. Just because you happen to think so, it doesn't mean that he has to follow your set of rules. Perhaps he wants to have someone to come back to . . . someone praying for him while he is away . . . someone who will be there to love him whatever happens.'

'You are a dreamer,' Adam said harshly, wishing she did not make it sound so inviting. 'In more cases than I care to recall, men under my command have had no one to go back to. Letters come in the thick of battle . . . lies to dull their minds when they need to be at their most alert. Excuses for sleeping with another man, or for the child not fathered by them . . . I have no illusions about an honest woman. I have yet to meet one!'

'You are a hard man. I think you have been alone too long. If, as I believe, Alída loves your brother, she will never betray him. No more would I destroy something as wonderful as she has found. You will see. She will make you eat your words.'

'And you, Natália? Would you remain at home, alone, waiting for your man? No wild rides across the countryside with gallant English officers—no *festas* to relieve the boredom?'

'Now you are laughing at me again! It is you who are the fool,' Natália stormed, and flung herself away from him as he put out a hand to catch hold of her. He followed, but made no other attempt to detain her until they were well away from the laughter and shouting as some of the *guerrilleros* began a mock bull-fight among themselves. Once the noise had receded, however, he lengthened his stride to keep pace with her. Although she knew she ought to stop and turn back, for there was no other person now in sight, Natália was too angry to consider it.

'I am going back to the house,' she snapped, not looking at him. His silence infuriated her still more. 'I do not need an escort.'

'Your sense of direction is appalling,' he drawled. 'We are going the wrong way.'

'Oh!' She halted so abruptly that he broke into laughter, and rested his back against a low wall to finish his black cigarette, as she looked about her to seek her bearings. So many lights confused her. 'Take me back!' she demanded.

'I did not bring you,' he reminded her. 'I'd rather like an answer to my question. Are you the kind of woman a man can trust? Could you be a loyal, loving wife and stay at home, when all about you your friends are going out enjoying themselves?'

'If I found a man to love . . . yes.' The answer came without hesitation. 'For you I would stay at home,' she whispered silently to the silent man opposite. 'If you asked it of me, I would follow you into battle, wash your clothes, mend your socks, tend your wounds. Just to be near you, I would risk death itself.'

As before, he read her mind with uncanny accuracy.

'Somehow I can't envisage those lovely soft hands blistered with hard work. If I loved a woman enough to marry her, I wouldn't want to leave her alone. I'd want her with me every moment of the day and night.' He straightened and came closer, peering into her upturned face. 'Nor would I subject her to the rigours of army life. You don't know what it's like . . . How can you? You are a lady, meant for better things.'

'When—when will you leave?' Natália's voice was barely audible. His words crushed her. She could not let him go without trying to make him understand what she felt. Even if he laughed at her again, he would know, and perhaps one day in the future, he would remember the village of Alto Verde and the girl who was willing to follow him to the ends of the earth.

'Tomorrow—at about noon. My men will all have thick heads, but that's never stopped them riding before. Drew and I are expected in Lisboa. If I know my father, a party awaits our arrival.'

'At your father's house?' He nodded. 'Take me with

you? I—I can stay with Alída when you return to Torres Vedras. I shall come with you, if you like. I have to get away from here before . . . before I die of suffocation!'

'You little idiot! You don't know what you are asking.' Adam's voice was so harsh that she flinched. 'What you ask is impossible. For one, your father would come after me with a loaded gun. God knows what he would do to you! Whatever possessed you to ask me that?'

'I can stay with Alída,' Natália repeated hollowly. 'I don't want to stay here. I can't . . . now.'

'Now?' His fingers fastened over her shoulders, biting into the soft skin beneath her blouse. 'Why—now? What are you trying to say, Natália? We have enjoyed each other's company these past few days, I admit it . . . But that's all. Don't try to make any more out of it. You will only hurt yourself with such delusions.'

At the same time as he uttered the words and felt her stiffen in pain, he knew they were a lie. She had given him much more than just her company or a few sweet smiles. She challenged the way he had chosen to live. Without realising it until this moment, he knew that life would never be the same without her. Yet what could he do? He balked at risking everything to take her with him . . . the consequences would not bear consideration. The scandal would harm her more than him, and he did not want to hurt her in any way. She was too precious to him.

With a fierce expletive, he tilted back her chin and saw tears glistening in her eyes.

'Don't say anything,' she begged. 'Just hold me. I know that what I ask is impossible. I must stay here, and you will leave. I shall never see you again . . . but we have these few moments more. Hold me . . . Let me pretend it could be otherwise.'

Tears soaked the velvet of the mask. She tore it away and buried her face against his shirt. For a moment he did not move—did not touch her. Then his arms closed round her tighter and tighter until, with something almost sounding like a groan of pain, he tipped back her head and kissed her with sudden turbulent passion. The kisses rained on her mouth and neck were not gentle as before, but fiercely demanding, intent on provoking a response from her. Had she wanted to resist, she found herself wondering what chance she would have stood against the experience imparted into every one, weakening her, battering down the defences which came under attack every moment they were together and were now shattered, leaving her defenceless. None! She had none now . . .

Her hands locked in total surrender behind his neck, her fingers toying with his thick short hair. The texture of it surprised her, for it was silky to the touch. She had expected it to be coarse—hard like the man himself. Why had she ever thought Adam Sorrell hard? Arrogant? Unfeeling? She sighed as she pressed closer against him, feeling the taut muscles of his chest against her breasts. She gave no thought to anything or anyone, save the sheer ecstasy of the moment and the man who held her. But Adam did. They stood in a narrow lane bordering open fields. On one side of a low stone wall were a cluster of almond trees in full bloom. He could see everything clearly, for there was a full moon which bathed the whole countryside in a silver sheen. If anyone came upon them . . .

Natália felt herself lifted and borne away. She opened her mouth to ask where he was taking her, but the words were never uttered. A moment more . . . two . . . alone with him, that was so little to ask when she would never see him again. The sweet aroma of fava beans planted on the far side of the fields reached her as he laid her down on thick, clover-dotted grass. She opened her eyes as he sprawled beside her, but it was too dark here to see the expression on his face. Beyond them the path was a bright as day, but here, beneath the heavily-laden boughs of the trees, was a cloak of darkness to hide them from prying eyes, to keep her secret from those who would run to her father and betray her, deprive her of these few most precious moments.

Detached by the wind, a shower of pink and white petals fluttered down upon them. With a soft chuckle, Adam brushed them from his hair and from her face. His fingers lingered on the smooth skin where several had settled just above the hollow of her breasts.

'I feel like the princess in the legend,' Natália said, her breath catching in her throat. 'Do you know the story?'

'Tell me,' he said quietly. He knew it well, but he did not want to break the spell that surrounded them. It was as though they were cocooned in another world all of their own. He wanted to listen to her voice, and to remember this night when he was back in the field, cold, hungry, dirty, fighting his own kind of war with his *guerrilleros*.

He knew, as she told him the legend of the sad princess, how much it meant to her. She, too, had dreams. He wanted to tell her he was no handsome prince come to sweep her off her feet, although had the world been his to give, he would have laid it before her as a silent admission of what was in his heart. He had never before found himself lost for words. It forced him to acknowledge how drastically—how forcefully—this slender, blue-eyed girl had thrust herself into his closed existence. She challenged everything he believed in . . .

'Why aren't you laughing at me?' Natália asked, her fingers lightly touching his cheek. Beneath the skin, although it was not visible with the deep tan, she could feel a scar slicing from eyebrow to chin. 'I think you have been in many battles,' she added, as he took her fingers and turned them palm upwards to plant a kiss there.

'An old sabre-wound. A French cuirassier tried to lop my head off. Why should I laugh at such a beautiful story? Do you think me an unfeeling brute?'

'Men don't seem to hold such store by these things as we women do. My father thinks I am a dreamer . . . he is always telling me so. I am a great disappointment to him, but I don't really know why. I never seem to please him. Even Alída thinks I am foolish. Oh, she doesn't say as much, but I see it in her eyes sometimes. But then she has been married to a cruel man who did not love her. I shall pray with your brother that she finds what she is looking for.'

'So shall I—for Drew's sake, as well as hers. I do not want my brother to be hurt,' Adam returned. 'Men have their dreams as well, you know! One day I shall own a *quinta* like this one. My vineyards will stretch as far as the eye can see. I shall build a fine house, with long archways to shelter the pátios. There will be flowers about the walls, and orchards . . .' He broke off, suddenly aware that he had never discussed his ambitious hopes with anyone. His father, even though they were close, took for granted that his eldest son would not only inherit the family business, but continue to greater things. Sorrell men had always had high ambitions and always achieved their set goals. Adam would be no different.

Drew also would do what he wanted—marry, raise a family and settle for a quiet English lifestyle in the country. He would be a village doctor and well content with his lot. Adam found himself wondering how Alída would fit into that picture—if at all.

'I should like to see your house when it is built,' Natália murmured. Hot tears pricked her eyes and she turned her head away, afraid he might feel them on his cheek. She would never see it, of course . . . nor him, after tonight.

'What is it, *menina*? Do you want me to take you back to the others?' He knew he should, but it was not what he wanted . . . Neither was it her choice, he realised, as she turned back to look up at him.

'No, I want to stay here with you for ever . . .' If only that were possible! No father, no Cesar, no marriage . . . Just the two of them, and her dreams. 'No one will miss me; that is why I am wearing Pilar's clothes. She went to bed, pretending to have a headache. When she reappears, she will stay well out of the way of . . . Father', she corrected herself in time. She had been about to say 'Cesar'. 'This was her idea. I don't know what I would have done without her. We could never have been alone, and I wanted to be with you,' she whispered shyly.

Adam laid his lips tenderly against hers. He felt the wetness of tears on her cheeks and was momentarily startled, but as she wound her arms about his neck and her lips flared to life beneath his, they were forgotten. With the barriers he himself had erected to keep them apart no longer able to withstand the onslaught of his own desires, he allowed himself the pleasure of holding her, exploring her trembling body with knowledgeable hands, plying her soft mouth with unrestrained kisses. He wanted this girl as he had wanted no other in his life before. Caution was thrown aside, and his cardinal rule discarded alongside. His fingers reached for the plait of red-gold hair, and began to unbraid it.

Carefully Pilar eased herself away from the figure sprawled beside her, who was snoring drunkenly. Holding together her torn bodice, she limped to the door and began to scream. Soon she was surrounded by men and women who needed only one look at her dishevelled condition, the mass of black hair where pieces of straw still clung, the bruises already beginning to show on her face and arms, to know the terrible thing that had happened. The tears which came, as questions filled the air, brought relief in the wake of what had been done to her.

Someone ran off to find Father José and Dom Abílio. Minutes later, both men came shouldering their way through the crowd surrounding her. Once again she blurted out how Cesar had dragged her into the stables and brutally attacked her. Curious faces peered in at the prostrate figure who still snored blissfully a few feet away, unaware of the storm about to erupt about him.

'Just a minute!' Abílio held up a hand, and immediately silence reigned. He was staring at the yellow gown Pilar wore, torn and dusty now, the beautiful lace which had once adorned it ripped away, hanging useless from sleeves and bodice. For one terrible moment when he had first come running in the wake of his servant, all he had seen was the bright colour. He had recognised it at once. Natália! His daughter had been attacked! Violated by the man he had chosen to care for her. It could not be! And then Pilar had turned to face him and he had felt a cold fury begin to rise inside him as he came to realise what had taken place. Natália had changed clothes with her maid, and Cesar, in his inebriated condition, not knowing the difference, had detained the wrong girl. 'Where is your mistress?'

No words of comfort for the traumatic experience Pilar had suffered, no kindness on the hard, brown face. He had to find Natália. Where was she? Who with?

'Oh, senhor . . . forgive me,' Pilar stammered, clutching at his hand, pressing it to her mouth. When he snatched it away, Father José looked at him reprovingly, not understanding his lack of concern over what had taken place. A vile act deserving of the harshest punishment. As the *juiz* of Alto Verde, it was his duty to arrest and deal with the culprit, no matter who he was. And there was no doubt of that. The priest cast his eyes away from Cesar, his mouth deepening in disgust. Why was there always one law for the rich and another for the poor? This was not the first village girl to have suffered at the hands of this man . . . and poor Dona Natália was to be his bride. Heaven forbid that such a sweet creature should be subjected to a monster like that!

'My daughter, where is she? Speak, woman! Do you think me a fool? You are wearing the gown she wore earlier . . . Tell me, or I'll take a whip to you now, and add a few more bruises to those he gave you!'

There were gasps of surprise at his harsh words, but then whispers and knowing glances went towards the tell-tale saffron gown. Horror began turning to speculation . . .

'She is not at fault, senhor. That English devil has bewitched her. She asked me to change clothes with her so that she could meet him without anyone knowing . . . It is God's retribution what has happened to me, for allowing her to make me obey her. I wanted to come to you, but he . . . he said he would set men to guard me if I did not do as she wanted. His men . . . the *guerrilleros*! I was afraid!'

'Which one, girl? Damn it, there are two of them!'

'Major Sorrell. She is with him.' Pilar covered her face with her hands as Abílio swung about calling for torches, ordering every street and alley to be searched, every garden and orchard combed until Natália was found. The *festa* was forgotten . . . even Cesar was momentarily excluded from their thoughts, until Father José spoke up, to regain everyone's attention.

'Is the man who attacked this poor girl to go free, Dom Abílio?'

Abílio Lareira barely looked at the shadowy figure sprawled in the straw. With Natália alone somewhere with the Englishman, nothing else was important to him, but he knew he had to say something to appease the angry faces thronging him. He knew also that there would be no marriage . . . no grandson for the Quinta das Raposeiras . . . at least not with this man.

'Carry him to the house. Lock him in his room and put a man to stand guard at the door. Until I return, he is to remain there. He shall pay for his crime, Father, never fear. As will the Englishman, if he has laid a hand on my daughter. Perhaps you should pray for them both.'

Pilar watched the torches disappear into the distance. From time to time the searchers called to each other, and children followed, still playing their games, not understanding the seriousness of this new adventure. Slowly she turned and went into the house. One of the young maids ran to help her, and led her into the kitchen, where she poured her some wine, and bathed the grazes and cuts on her skin and tried, unsuccessfully, not to ask too many questions.

She received no answers, and began to wonder if the shock had not turned Pilar's mind. She sat by the window like a statue, gazing out into the darkness, not touching her wine or the tit bits of food offered, and sympathetic words fell on deaf ears. Occasionally she touched the cut at one side of her mouth, and a strange smile would flit across the dark features.

Half an hour later the torches reappeared, coming back towards the house. Only then did Pilar come back to life. Still without a word, she climbed to her feet and went upstairs to await the return of her mistress. It was possible that Natália would never forgive her for what she had done, but she had achieved her aim . . . She had seen that by the look of disgust on Dom Abílio's face that Cesar would never become his son-in-law.

Natalia became aware of voices in the distance . . . shouting . . . calling her name. No, she was mistaken. With Pilar in her place, who would come looking for her? Golden chains and necklaces lay in a heap on top of the black velvet jacket on the grass beside her. Her blouse was open to the waist baring firm young breasts to Adam's tantalising caresses. She moaned as his lips seared her bare skin, her senses clamouring for his touch, more of the soul-searching kisses which reduced her to a quivering reed in his arms.

The consequences of her actions had long since vanished from her mind. She refused to accept that anything so wonderful could be wrong or sinful. Yet she was about to give herself to a man who would never marry her . . . It *was* sinful! Damned to the eternal fires of hell, her soul would be forever lost. She fought and lost the battle to push Adam away, to snatch up her things and flee from his presence. Instead, she brushed a kiss across the dark hair on his chest, inwardly wondering at her boldness as she did so, but there were no longer any chains binding her to convention, to the behaviour of a lady . . . love had freed her to be herself.

'When you go, wherever you go, I shall pray for you, Adão. I shall never love a man as I love you!'

She felt the whole of his body stiffen in shock. He drew back from her, peering down into her shadowed features. Love! She had said she loved him! Was that what he felt for her? Unwittingly she had spoken the only words which could have brought him to his senses, forced him to struggle for some composure. Love was something he had not dared allow himself even to contemplate. Tomorrow he would be gone from her life. There was more than a slight possibility that he could be killed or seriously wounded in the fighting to come. Either way, she would suffer because she had known him.

'Do I offend you with the truth? I am sorry. Do not be angry . . . I ask nothing from you. You have told me how you feel about being tied to one woman.' She made it sound like being sentenced to a chain-gang for life, Adam thought, his mouth tightening at the break in her voice. That was how he had once considered marriage, but with this girl it could be so different . . . 'I shall be content with tonight . . . At least, let me have that . . .'

Natália did not see the figures creeping up on them until it was too late, and several dark shapes loomed over Adam's back. She cried out as something—she could not see what, but the sound it made as it connected with the back of his head made nausea rise in her stomach—was brought down with great force. He slumped across her with a groan, his weight pinning her to the ground. But it was for a moment only. A torch was thrust downwards, and Adam was hauled away from her to slump unconscious in the grasp of two of her father's servants.

Abílio himself reached down and, grasping her by the wrist, pulled her unceremoniously to her feet. She cried out in pain as the flat of his hand struck her across first one cheek and then the other. This, too, with such force that she would have fallen had he not been holding her.

Through eyes swimming with tears, she saw her father rake her from head to toe, his face growing bleak at the sight of her loose hair, the gaping blouse and crumpled skirts. Then lifted to stare bleakly at Adam's open shirt. Slowly his gaze passed on to the faces of the watchful villagers, who were silent witnesses to the disgrace his daughter had brought upon his house. Rolling in the grass like a common street woman! And, from what he had heard as he crept up on them, wanting more . . . enjoying it!

'Have you nothing to say for yourself, girl?' he thundered. Natália winced as he raised his clenched fist, terrified she was about to be struck again.

Alída materialised from the shadows behind him, caught his arm, and said in a low, but controlled voice, 'Not here, Father. Must we air our dirty linen in public? Let me take her back to the house. We can deal with her there.'

Abílio hesitated. It was too late to worry how many people knew about this disgraceful incident. Many had seen and heard, and those who had not would be told before morning. But if the slightest whisper leaked out of Alto Verde, the whole village would pay, and they knew it.

Natália clutched at the front of her blouse. Alída fastened the ribbons for her, not meeting her sister's eyes. Was she ashamed of her, too, Natália wondered in horror? Was she not going to Lisboa with Drew Sorrell? Opening her house so that they could be together . . . She had no right!

'Yes, the house,' Abílio muttered absently, still staring at the unconscious Adam. 'This matter must be settled quickly. I hope you realise he is a dead man, my girl,' he said, as he flung his daughter into her sister's outstretched arms and turned on his heel. He did not speak to her again on the agonisingly slow return to the house, hemmed in by silent villagers who gradually slipped away to tell their own version of the story to others who had left the *festa* early. The way they looked at Natália sickened her. Only one or two expressions betrayed sympathy for her plight. They were all too afraid of her father to take her side, she realised.

Alída helped her upstairs to her room, where they found Pilar waiting to take her mistress in her arms and offer the first real comfort she had been offered. So great was her agitation as she dwelt on her father's words that she at first did not notice the bruises and cuts on the maid's face. Hours later, as shock began to recede, a terrifying numbness came in its place. She sat in a chair with Alída on one side of her, trying in vain to offer words of consolation. What could she say? Nothing mattered now except to appease their father's wrath somehow . . . and ensure that no harm came to Adam Sorrell.

'I hope you realise he is a dead man.' As she recalled the words, Natália grew so pale and agitated that both women with her thought she might faint. Pilar fetched a glass of sweet lemonade for her to drink. As she took it, Natália became aware of the marks on the brown face, and the maid knew that the time had come to tell her what else had taken place that evening.

'Leave us, I wish to speak to her alone,' Abílio said from the open doorway. Pilar slipped past him without a backward glance at the dejected figure still sitting in the chair, but once outside, she took up a position close enough to the door to hear if Dom Abílio used more violence against his daughter. Not even he would be allowed to lay another finger on her!

'Father, she knows about Pilar. Hasn't she suffered enough?' Alída begged, rising to her feet. She dared not disobey the command, although she did not know what lay in store for her poor sister. A convent; most likely. For Adam Sorrell, there was the likelihood of a duel with her father, and probably with Cesar too . . . the man was vain enough to call out his rival even after what he had done. He, of all people, would be the one to suffer least from all this, she suspected. 'Let it end here, for all our sakes.'

'It will end when my name has been vindicated . . . and her name is not besmirched with mud. *Deus!* Why did He allow this to happen? Leave us.'

As the door closed behind her sister, Natália raised her head. Taking a deep breath, she looked her father directly in the eyes with an open defiance that inwardly shocked him. A moment ago she had looked afraid, dejected, full of remorse. Now that they were alone, they were enemies again . . . and she was prepared to fight him.

'I am not ashamed that for a little while I lay in the arms of the man I love. You had no right to expect me to marry Cesar, share his bed, bear his children, knowing how I felt about him. I hate him, do you hear? I loathe the very sight of him. I shall take the veil rather than stand by his side and hear Father José make us man and wife. I would rather die!'

Her voice faltered and broke. Tears swam in her blue eyes, but she brushed them away before he thought them a show of weakness. She must be strong . . . and save Adam somehow.

'There will be no marriage between you,' Abílio replied heavily. Crossing to the window, he stared down into the courtyard. A few villagers still lingered by the well and beneath the trees, casting furtive glances towards the house. Damn them and their curiosity! he fumed. They were waiting and watching to see what he would do, what punishment he would pronounce on the man who had defiled his daughter.

It was ironic, he thought, how fate had given him the chance to eradicate the mistakes he had made. Natália did not want Cesar. Now she did not have to have him. He would give her what she really wanted, a token gesture of the unacclaimed affection he still held back so well from both his daughters. His eyes narrowed as they came to rest on Natália's flushed cheeks. He could not get the vision of her lying in Sorrell's arms out of his mind . . . the open blouse, the tousled hair, the skirts and petticoats riding high about her slender thighs. The child had become a woman without him realising it!

'It had to happen. The fault was mine. I should not have allowed you to talk me into a long betrothal. You should have married Cesar last year, and you would have a child to occupy your time. It is too late now.'

'A child by an animal who has just raped my maid?' Natália flung back. 'That's all you care about, isn't it? A child . . . an heir . . . you will never have one now!' She straightened and slowly came to her feet, her eyes growing wide. 'What do you mean . . . I am not going to marry Cesar? He has freed me?'

'I would not have allowed it anyway, after what has happened, but yes, he has given you back to me. He does not wish to have soiled goods.' The rush of colour which came to Natália's cheeks deepened his belief that he had come upon her and her lover too late. Why was it always too late? His fault? Yes, his entirely . . . But had he told her what troubled him, could she have understood, until this moment when something inside her reared its head, urging rebellion against everything she had been taught. His fault . . . But not *all* his. 'Do you want this man? This Major Adam Sorrell? I heard you say you loved him. You know nothing of love, believe me . . . Even less of men like the Major. You could not hold him for a moment away from here, when he is with his own kind . . . Would you be prepared to suffer his contempt until the day you die? That will be the price you will pay.'

'I would pay any price to be with him . . . follow him anywhere! It does not matter that he does not love me. I love him. I always shall. Do what you want with me, I don't care, so long as you do not harm him. I know you will not believe me, but nothing happened . . . not in the way you think. If you had not found us . . .' She nodded her head. 'Yes, I would have belonged to him, and not regretted it for an instant. Why could you not have found a man like Adam for me? He will not drag me to some mausoleum in Setúbal and parade me before his friends like a useless ornament! You would have had your precious grandson, Father, but he would not have lived here. You would have been totally alone. You could not have taught him to love the vines as you do. Possibly you would see him two or three times a year, if you were lucky. Adam loves the land, and he would have grown to love this place. I think he already has—and me, had I been free. I would have made it happen. He could love me. I know it!'

'And if it did not happen? What kind of life would you have?'

'Better than one I would share with Cesar. A life with the man I love. I promise that you would have had many, many fine sons.'

At the ensuing silence, Natália fell back into the chair. What was he going to do? Challenge Adam? Abílio was a fair shot; was Adam better? If either were killed or injured, it would be her fault . . . And then there was

Cesar. He would demand satisfaction because he knew it was expected of him. He had to maintain the façade of being the grossly injured party. The outrage of Pilar's body was of little importance.

'What are you going to do?' she cried, as he turned towards the door. 'Blame me, if anyone must be blamed. I ask no mercy for myself, for I know there is none in you to give. You have never loved me. But do not hurt a good and kind man because of that dislike. Let him go. We shall never see him again.'

'Change into some respectable clothes and come downstairs. If you have no wish to see blood spilled on your account, you will do exactly as I tell you, do you understand?'

Mutely Natália nodded, her hopes rising. Did this mean that there would be no duel . . . for any of them?

'Swear it?' Abílio demanded, and the words dropped from her lips like a death-knell, as she was committing herself to whatever he decided.

'I swear it.'

'The past will not rule me in this decision, or my own desires. You have chosen your man.' At his words, Natália felt the room reel unsteadily around her. What was he telling her? 'You shall be married tonight.'

'No!' she screamed. 'No!' It was the one thing Adam would never agree to! But her father had already gone.

CHAPTER FIVE

'ADAM, ARE you all right?' It was Drew's voice, but coming from a long way off. Adam opened his eyes, but a thousand coloured lights exploded inside his brain, and with a groan he slumped in the high-backed chair where he had been deposited by the two villagers who had brought him back to the house. Then, addressing someone else, 'Did your man have to hit him so hard?'

'Under the circumstances, I would not say unnecessary force was used.' The voice of Abílio Larcira, cold and distant.

Where the hell was he? Adam wondered. It was impossible to remember anything while someone was wielding a hammer with great gusto inside his head. Had he been drinking? Did he recall dancing—music—a girl? He shook his head to try and clear it, and winced in pain. 'The man has known my daughter since she was born. To come across her, being—manhandled—by a stranger! He acted quite within his rights. Any man from this village would have done the same.'

'Manhandled be damned!' Drew snapped. He rarely lost his temper, but he was close to it now. Of all women to get involved with, Adam had to choose the daughter of the local judge. A girl about to be married, although he suspected that his brother was unaware of that fact. He had been played for a fool. It was not like him to fall so easily for a pair of blue eyes. He was a cautious man, who usually chose his women with great care. A snatch at pleasure, such as his men enjoyed, was not his way. And yet . . . he could not believe it! 'Your daughter didn't look as if she was exactly being forced, senhor. I was there, remember. I heard her, too!'

'You heard nothing, Captain Sorrell. For your own sake, as well as that of the Major, I suggest you remember that.'

Manhandled? Girl? Forced? What the devil were they talking about? Adam struggled to rise above the pain and nausea engulfing him, opened his eyes and lifted an unsteady hand to the back of his throbbing head. Someone had hit him? He had a lump there the size of an ostrich egg. He blinked several times before being able to acertain that he was in a room where bookshelves lined every wall. Behind a large carved oak desk sat Abílio Lareira. His features were rigid with anger as he gazed across the room towards him.

'You are recovering, Major Sorrell. Good.' He did not sound as though he cared one way or the other, Adam thought, relieved that the mists were clearing from his vision. 'Pour your brother a large brandy, Captain. I am sure he needs it. And one for yourself. Then let us bring a swift conclusion to this ugly affair.'

'Thanks.' Adam reached for the glass Drew handed him with a grateful smile. It was more like a grimace, for it hurt even to make that small gesture. 'Would someone mind telling me what is going on? Nothing is clear . . .'

'How convenient. However, loss of memory will get you nowhere,' Abílio remarked drily.

Adam swallowed the brandy without appreciation. Pictures began to flash through his mind . . . of a girl with burnished gold curls, large eyes the colour of sapphires . . . He had been holding her, making love to her, when . . .

Drew saw the sudden dawning of reality mirrored in the pain-filled eyes, and said steadily, 'You were with Dona Natália tonight, Adam . . .'

'Yes. We've been together since the wedding, dancing and enjoying ourselves.' He was still dazed and not too careful with his words. He had nothing to hide! 'What's wrong with that? I don't see you with a lump on your head or an irate father breathing down your neck, and we were about the same thing!'

'Dona Natália is bethrothed, Adam. To Dom Cesar Duarte, the man you exchanged insults with tonight. She had no right to be with you, and she knew it. She even changed clothes to avoid being recognised because she knew the mischief she was causing with her foolishness.'

'Mischief?' Adam echoed. Betrothed—to that boor? She had said she loved him! Or had he imagined it? No, she had told him very little about herself, he realised, forcing himself over the pain in order to concentrate. He held out his empty glass. Drew took it and refilled it without looking at Abílio or asking his permission. The older man said nothing, and motioned back the servant who moved to intercept him. 'Where is she? Bring her in here, and she will clear me of whatever nasty suspicions are lurking in your mind, senhor. We spent a pleasant evening together—nothing else happened. You have my word.'

'If you swore it to me on the Holy Bible, it would make no difference,' he was told. 'You were found with my daughter in a most compromising situation. Her honour is at stake. The honour of my name, Major Sorrell. I intend neither to be tarnished because you do not know the difference between a lady of good blood and a *tasca* whore.'

The last words brought Adam to his feet, grey flints of steel glinting in the narrowed eyes.

'A lady does not become betrothed to one man and tell another she loves him,' he flung back, swaying unsteadily. Drew put out a hand to steady him, but it was brushed aside. Adam lurched to the desk where Abílio sat, and leaned upon it heavily, glaring at the man who had confronted him with such a devastating accusation. 'Nor does she seek him out. Yes, senhor, your daughter did the seeking.' '. . . and would have been willing to a great deal more if they had not been interrupted,' he almost said. Somehow he stopped himself.

Why was he so angry? He had been suspicious of her in the first place. No one could be as innocent as that—and he was right! She had flirted with him, teased him with a non-existent virtue that had brought him to the very brink of casting aside his doubts and carefully made plans . . . of declaring that he was wrong . . . and so lonely. He had never admitted it to himself before, and the knowledge shocked him deeply. How many nights had he lain awake, listening to his men discussing their wives and families? For those who received distressing letters from home, there were double that number who were happily married and had fine bonny children. He wanted that, too. A wife, a home, children. And for the first time in his life he had found a woman he was willing to give up everything for. His ambitions could wait . . . she would come first. His heart had ruled his head, and look where it had got him! Fool! Blind idiot! He was worse than any of his men . . . he who had so confidently mapped out the perfect future. He felt betrayed! He berated himself in silent agony of mind. She had lied, had tricked him . . . God, how his head hurt!

He walked back to the chair and sat down, took the second brandy and drank it more slowly than the first, feeling it begin to clear the last of the cobwebs from his mind. Drew saw the coldness that settled over the berry-brown features, the diamond frost which appeared in the depths of the grey-green eyes, and swallowed hard. His brother was angry. Dangerously angry! He wished he could have warned their men of these developments, but he had been thrust into the library with as much lack of ceremony as Adam himself. Alída had whispered to him, before she was ordered upstairs, something about a marriage to put everything right. If that did not happen . . . Adam faced the possibility of being challenged by both Dom Abílio and the man Natália was to marry. In the unlikely event he survived, he would be turned over to the villagers—as the last French soldier who had ravished a girl had been.

It was all some ghastly mistake, Adam found himself thinking. He could not have been so wrong about her. He had held her, felt the hesitant, almost child-like, responses from her soft lips, the endearments she whispered as he caressed her. An innocent—or a talented actress? No. In a moment she would burst through the door and tell her father the truth, that he had not stolen her virtue . . . If she was innocent, why then had she not told him of the other man? Why had she deliberately sought him out the morning they rode together, challenged him to a race, and further aroused his interest in her? Everything she had done, from the first moment they met in this house, had been in a deliberate attempt to focus his attention on her. No innocent, but a witch with the face of an angel.

He concluded that she must have done this kind of thing many times before; why else was it so natural to her? Others had come before him, others would follow him, even after her marriage. His condemnation of her helped to assuage his shattered pride . . . and his anger settled like a protective mantle over the chasm that had once been his heart. All these thoughts and many more, as he dwelt on the brief time they had shared, passed behind an implacable mask through which no one else could see. Years of soldiering, of accepting death as an everyday part of life, had hardened him, taught him to control his emotions before others. *She* had roused in him a passion he did not even know existed! Damn her! Damn her to hell!

'Exactly what kind of retribution do you think you will bring down on my head, senhor?' he enquired in a cool, insolent tone that made Abílio's mouth tighten. Struck down from behind by a blow that would have kept a lesser man unconscious for hours, accused of heavens knows what—he was still in control of himself. Abílio momentarily acknowledged that Natália had been right. Why could he not have found a man like this as a husband for her? Drew became more uneasy, knowing his brother was at his most deadly when he was angry, but polite, suffering insults without striking back. Like a jungle animal, he could pounce without warning to crush his prey.

'Dom Abílio, I assure you my brother is not a liar. If he says your daughter was . . .' A look from across the desk froze him.

'Was what, Captain? Would you have me believe that a young girl of barely eighteen years, brought up in the seclusion of this household, a devout Catholic girl who has been betrothed to the same man since she was six, has spent all her years preparing for the day when she would be his wife . . .' He came to his feet. Although he was not tall, he seemed to fill the room with his fury. Neither Drew nor Adam were aware the display was made more dramatic by the added guilt that he himself felt. This was his last chance to prove not only to Natália, but to himself, that he was capable of caring. '. . . would openly flirt with another man, a stranger? She offered hospitality, as I would expect her to . . . polite conversation . . . Major Sorrell took advantage of her youth and her inexperience to perpetrate his seduction. No doubt he has had many such diversions that have provided him with amusement to alleviate the boredom of war. This one will cost him dear.'

'Need I remind you that your daughter changed clothes with her maid so that neither you nor Senhor Duarte would know she was slinking out to meet me?' Adam interrupted.

'As you suggested she should. Her maid has confessed everything to me. It was your idea.'

'And what is Natália's version?' Adam demanded. So the maid was in it, too? A pretty trap he had fallen into!

He looked away, ignoring Drew's warning glance. The anger in him was controlled, but he wanted an end to this farce. He was tired and his head hurt. All he wanted now was to sleep and then to leave first thing in the morning. 'Never mind. She had already shown me what an accomplished liar she is, so I expect she has some tale concocted for you. If you wish for satisfaction, senhor, if you refuse to accept my word that your daughter is as pure as the day she came into this world, I am at your service. After you, I shall accommodate the other one, if he has the stomach for it.'

'Adam, have you lost your mind?' Drew said, running a hand distractedly through his unruly hair. 'You cannot fight two duels! Besides, there is no need, if you . . .'

'If I what?' His brother turned and stared at him from beneath arched black brows. 'Apologise for something I have not done? Ordinarily I would not, but if it will get us all out of here at first light, I shall. Under duress.'

'It is not as simple as you seem to think, Major Sorrell.' Abílio reseated himself. He felt safer on the far side of the desk, where Adam could not reach him. As those eyes fastened on him, he had visions of him launching himself across the space between them, those lean, strong fingers closing round his neck. 'There is only one way out of this for you. You will marry Natália tonight.'

'The devil I will! I'll join him in hell first,' Adam swore, but he did not move. The only indication of the shock he had received was a tiny pulse which began to beat rapidly along the line of his scarred cheek.

'If that is your wish, that is what will happen. Do you know what happened to the last soldier who molested a girl in this village?' Abílio's voice was very quiet, perfectly controlled. He was astute enough to suspect, although his threats did not frighten Adam, that he would choose life before death. He was a good soldier, he had seen death, and survived. He knew how pleasant life was . . . 'The villagers caught him. I could do nothing . . . They put him in the middle of a haycart and set light to it. He tried to run, of course, but he was driven back by pitchforks and axes. An unpleasant death, do you not agree?'

'If I do not walk out of this house very, very soon, senhor, my men will hear what has happened and they will come and fetch me. They have muskets and pistols —perhaps you had not noticed. And they are not above slitting the throat of anyone who gets in their way.'

'I believe you. Men would die . . . men who do not deserve to die because of your stubbornness, your refusal to accept that you must pay for your—indiscretion. A gentleman would not hesitate. You call yourself a gentleman, do you not? Your conduct with my daughter leads me to wonder otherwise, but . . .'

'Marriage to her would allow you to overlook your disapproval.' Adam's mouth deepened into a sardonic smile with no humour in it. 'No, thank you. I shall remain a swine.'

'Perhaps you would care to consider the—shall we say—alternatives? Marriage on the one hand, which will bring you not only Natália's large dowry, but this *quinta* when I die . . . and a considerable amount of money and property for your children.'

'Perhaps I am already a father,' Adam drawled, and his expression grew noticeably grimmer. He was beginning to believe the judge had a hand in it, too. Perhaps he and Natália had planned it together. Had Cesar Duarte thrown her over, discovered her little escapades with the others and broken off the engagement? Disgraced before the whole village—now that would make them put their heads together! They were both as proud as Hades!

'The alternative is to walk out of here, and take your chances with the villagers. I shall be upstairs comforting my daughter, and unable to intervene until it is unfortunately too late.' He was a judge, the most respected man in the village. His reputation for fair dealing was known far and wide. Never would he have allowed a hair of Adam's head to be touched, but the Major did not know this. He sounded the injured father, demanding justice for his innocent daughter. Adam would never know how Abílio fought down the urge to set him free, walk out of the room and do no more. Cesar would leave Alto Verde, never to return. Natália would retire to a convent and take the veil . . . and he would never have a grandson, an heir for his beloved home.

'You—a judge—would turn me over to be murdered?' Pain returned to Adam's brain as he tried desperately to find a way out of this maze of intrigue and treachery. Marry Natália? Make that lying little bitch his wife? 'You forget my men.'

'No, I do not, Major. Neither do I forget your brother, the Captain, who will be a witness to your very unpleasant demise. I shall have to discredit him in the eyes of his superiors, of course, but that will not be too difficult. I, also, have friends in high places. Your men will be told you left in the night . . . to elope with my daughter to Lisboa. They will try to catch up with you on the road. Please do nothing foolish,' Abílio hastened to say, as Adam began to rise from the chair, a murderous gleam in his eyes. To threaten him was one thing, but to involve Drew! 'There is a servant behind you, and he is armed. I do not want you rendered unconscious again, or you will not be able to stand upright for your wedding.'

'There will be no wedding,' Adam grated. 'Give her to Duarte with my compliments. Returned untouched— unwanted—unfulfilled.'

Abílio sighed and got to his feet. Carefully he went to the door and put his hand upon the handle before looking back at the seated man. Drew's hand had come down reassuringly, comfortingly, on his brother's shoulder. A solid front against the enemy, but it would avail them naught. Natália would have the man she wanted, he was sure of that.

'I shall speak with Father José. He will need a little time to speak with Natália before she comes down. Clean clothes will be sent to you here, Major Sorrell. I am sure you want to look your best for the occasion.'

Adam swore. Long and hard. Drew stood in an uncomfortable silence until he had finished. The servant followed Abílio, leaving them alone.

'You have to do it,' Drew muttered at last when his brother relapsed into silence.

'Marry her? Did you not hear me say I would not? She lied—her maid, too. God knows what they are about, the pair of them! As for that old man . . . I felt like throttling him! If I didn't feel so weak, I might have tried it.'

'You wouldn't have got as far as the desk. There was a great ape behind you with a pistol in his belt. Do you think he's bluffing? About the bonfire? I don't. I've heard what these Portuguese villagers do to the enemy.'

'We are supposed to be on their side,' Adam retorted, gingerly examining his head. His fingers came away with traces of blood on them. 'Get me some water and a cloth.' The words were hardly out of his mouth when the door opened again and a woman appeared. She placed a bowl of water and several linen cloths on the desk, and scuttled out again without a word.

'Does everyone believe I went off my head and attacked his daughter?' Adam demanded, the anger rising in him again. 'What has she said? Where is she?'

'In her room. Dom Abílio has spoken to her, that's all I know. And Alída . . . But when I tried to ask her what went on up there, she ran from me. From *me*, Adam! Damn it, man, we are going to get married as soon as possible.'

'God help you,' came the unsympathetic reply. 'Open your eyes. They are both looking for husbands, that's all.'

'Natália already has one in the offing,' Drew reminded him. 'What are we going to do?'

'We? Nothing. You stay out of this. Take the men and leave tonight. I'll do what has to be done, and follow you tomorrow.'

'No, I'm not leaving you to be roasted alive. What has to be done? Are you going to marry the girl, then? Whatever you decide, I am standing with you!'

He was a doctor, bound by oath to save lives, not to take them, although in the course of the bloody conflicts since he came to Portugal, he had found himself with a pistol or sabre in his hand, and had killed to save his own life and that of others. He abhorred violence. He was a simple man, torn from his medical studies and a dedicated vow to heal. Not a born leader like his brother, although he had never envied Adam his command.

He knew only too well the agony of mind that was endured over the loss of a single man in combat—the frustration suffered under well-meaning but ignorant fools who over-ruled him with their rank and were so often proved to be in error. His judgment was impeccable. In the jungle he would have been a king among wild animals—a veritable lion. The Spanish *guerrilleros* who rode under his command called him just that: Sorrell—*El León*. Not without good reason!

'What happened to all those merry widows in Lisboa you were going back to see? "Don't get serious," you told me. "Take one day at a time. Never get so involved you can't walk away from them." What happened?'

Adam came out of his chair so suddenly and with such violence that Drew stepped back in alarm.

'Damn you, Drew! Not now . . . Don't you think I've had enough?'

'You—you do feel something for her?' His brother's voice dropped to a mere whisper. He could never remember seeing his brother so vulnerable, with such pain in those hard eyes that it wiped away the hardness and anger. But it was gone in an instant. When he turned to look at Drew again, his expression was unreadable, his thoughts hidden from the one person with whom he had always shared everything.

'I marry the girl tonight. You can be my best man. Tomorrow we leave. Tell the men to get ready to ride at dawn. Don't stand there as if I had just delivered the sermon on the mount! See to this head, and then find Nuno. He will bring me some clothes.' He turned away again, and Drew was not quite sure he heard the final muttered words correctly. He hoped not. 'She will rue the day she decided to play games with me!'

'I can't!' Natália said in a trembling voice as she neared the library door. 'Father cannot force him to marry me. It's too—too degrading.'

'It's what you want,' Pilar hissed in her ear, the hold on her arm tightening. 'It's the Englishman—or Dom Cesar. Which would you rather have?'

'Cesar will never have me now . . . I would not have him!' she declared, her troubled gazed resting on the bruises on the face of her maid. The numbness she had felt upstairs was still with her, dulling her senses. She had sent word to her father, begging him to allow her a few minutes alone with Adam, but the only answer that came back was one demanding her presence in the library. She knew what it meant. Adam had agreed to marry her. Perhaps everything would be all right, after all. She could explain her reticence in telling him about Cesar. From what had taken place tonight with poor Pilar, he would understand her loathing of the man, her desire to keep him out of her life and her thoughts for as long as possible. She loved Adam, and surely he must care for her if he was willing to go through with the ceremony.

Father José urged her gently forward, mistaking her reluctance to enter as natural under the circumstances. He would say an extra Paternoster at his prayers tonight to include not only Dona Natália, but the arrogant young officer who was about to become her husband, Dom Cesar, still sleeping off his drunkeness upstairs . . . and Dom Abílio, in his hour of great torment.

'Alída, tell me what to do!' Natália cried, stretching out her hand. Her sister came from behind to grasp it comfortingly.

'You know what you have to do. You have no other choice. You chose Adam Sorrell the first time you laid eyes on him, though I never thought it would happen this way. I had visions of you eloping with him to Lisboa and me hiding the pair of you until Father's temper had cooled. Does it matter, my dear? He is yours, now. If you love him, you must convince him you had no deception in mind when you . . . sought his company.' At the sight of the alarm which leapt to her sister's face, Alída sighed. 'I think you should know . . . Adam believes the worst of you. That you deliberately lied to him, and flirted with him because you were bored. Drew has told me he truly thinks . . . you have had other men.'

If she had struck Natália, the girl could not have looked more stunned. The horror which slowly crept into the wide blue eyes declared her innocence, and the devastation the words had caused. If only Adam could have seen it, Alída thought. He must—or her poor sister would be subjected to the kind of marriage she herself had endured. She did not believe him cruel enough to beat her, but there was cruelty in him—she had sensed that—a ruthlessness Natália could have no way of combating. Her love would make her a tool in his hands . . .

'How—how could he? He was so gentle when he held me . . .' she broke off, aware of the growing frown on the face of the priest beside her. What had she done to make everyone believe the worst of her? The idyllic dream she had been experiencing these past days was suddenly turning into a hideous nightmare.

Alída opened the door, and Father José propelled Natália gently but firmly inside. Abílio stood behind his desk, with Drew and Adam in front of it. There were four servants in the room, she noticed. Two on either side of the brothers—like guards! Drew turned slightly, smiled at Alída, ignored her sister. He believed the worst of her, too, Natália thought, her steps faltering. Would no one believe in her innocence? She was in love! What was wrong in that? The man she loved would be her husband in a few short minutes . . . it was a dream come true!

Adam spun about on his heel without warning, and stared long and hard into her face. His narrowed eyes were like two flints of steel, edged with a fine border of glittering emerald. There was no smile on his face, no welcome. His suspicions, his coldness, reached out to her, causing her to shiver.

'Tell them the truth,' he said harshly.

Where was the kind, romantic man who had held her in his arms and spoken of his plans for the future? Where was the prince who had brushed the almond petals from her blouse and hair? Where was the lover who had taken her lips by storm and shown her how to be a woman? Who had taught her about love?

'She has told me all I need to know,' Abílio interposed cuttingly.

'I asked for the truth,' Adam grated, his gaze never leaving Natália's now ashen face. They penetrated to her soul . . . Could he not see the love there? Was he so blind? Or had his sweet words meant nothing? She had begun to believe that he had cared, she would have staked her life on it! Yet to look at him now! Hatred . . . contempt . . . but not love . . . or anything near! She had thought it would not matter. She loved him, she would make him love her. Now she saw it was impossible. He looked at her as if she was the lowest creature on earth.

'I have no wish to marry this man, Father,' she said in a dull voice. She cared not who heard her. A flicker of surprise showed in Adam's eyes, then it was replaced by derision. This, too, was an act, he believed. 'I shall retire to the Convent of Our Lady of Souls, if you will allow it. I shall bring no more shame on your name or on your house.'

Beside her, Alída gasped and looked to their father pleadingly. Pilar's grip tightened so much on Natália's arm that she would have flinched in pain, had she felt it. But she felt nothing. She was enveloped by a cold, chilling wind which numbed her to the bone, froze her brain. The burning passion in her heart killed the unrequited love.

'So, you admit you were at fault,' Adam breathed.

'A meaningless gesture to protect you! Foolish child, it will do no good. Had the Major been the gentleman he pretends, he would have accepted full responsibility long ago. It was the only decent thing to do,' Abílio retorted. His heart went out to his daughter, for her words told him she did truly love Adam Sorrell. Would he ever learn to care for her, he wondered, casting his eyes back to the Englishman's bleak features. 'Father José, you will begin. Come closer, Natália. Stand beside your man. Are you ready, Major Sorrell?''

Adam said nothing. He felt Natália move close alongside him. Her arm brushed his. Immediately he stepped a little to one side, and without looking at her, knew her cheeks had become bright red with embarrassment. What did she expect? Affection? Politeness? Even that would be an effort, but it would not be for long. Tomorrow Alto Verde would be far behind him and he would forget her. In Lisboa he would have the marriage annulled quickly and quietly, and then go out and get beautifully, hopelessly drunk! He gave a curt nod. Mute acceptance—nothing more. She was lucky to get that. If he alone had been involved, he would have taken his chances with the rabble outside . . . and Abílio's threats, but there was his brother to consider. Drew was stubborn enough to stay at his side and help him. And then his men would stay too, and some would be hurt. No, he would not risk anyone else becoming a casualty in this sordid affair. The responsibility was his alone, and he would deal with it—and Natália Lareira—in his own way!

'That's enough, Pilar. He won't notice what I look like,' Natália said tiredly. Her head had begun to ache from the wine she had consumed with Adam during the evening. She was not used to so much in such a short time. Was that why she had acted so shamelessly while in his arms, she wondered? No, she had no excuses. She had wanted him to make love to her. The wine had relaxed her and lessened her self-consciousness, but that was all. The maid was brushing her hair, and was only a quarter of the way through the one hundred strokes given morning and night. She continued with what she was doing with a sharp clicking noise of her tongue.

'You are a woman. Make him notice you!' she returned.

'Haven't I done enough to him already? This is all my fault.' Natália looked down at the gold band on her wedding finger that Alída had provided for the ceremony. She was the wife of Adam Sorrell. To do with as he wished. The thought frightened her. A woman, Pilar said. At this moment she had never felt less a woman, less sure of herself. She could have everything she wanted, yet she was too afraid to reach out and take it. She did not want to see the contempt in his eyes or bear the whiplash of his scorn, although she deserved both.

'We are both to blame. I, for allowing myself to think my dreams could come true, and you for aiding me in my stupidity. You could have prevented this had you not told Father I was alone with him . . .' She had to hit back at someone to compensate for her fear of unhappiness, even though she knew the maid should not have been the recipient of her bitterness.

'Do you think, once he saw me in your dress, that he did not know?' Pilar flung back, and through the mirror Natália saw her dark eyes flash with sudden anger. 'I have given you what you want. Him! You are a fool if you don't use every weapon you have to keep him. Look at you! Sitting here like a lost sheep waiting to be found and comforted by the shepherd. He will offer you no sympathy—no consolation. Don't wait for him to make the first move. Take the initiative . . .'

Natália's cheeks flushed at the rebuking tone. Icily she snapped, 'You forget yourself! Leave me.'

'Perhaps I shall do that.' Pilar put down the brush, her face hostile.

Still looking at her through the mirror, Natália thought how old she suddenly looked, as though some great burden were weighing down her shoulders and she could not rid herself of it. Immediately she was contrite, and spun about to catch her by the hand.

'Forgive me! I do not know what made me say such a thing. We are friends, and nothing must spoil that. I need you now, more than ever. When I leave here and am alone with him . . .'

'I know. Don't worry, I shall not abandon you, but you have come too far to turn back now. You have to make him believe you love him. You do, don't you?'

'When I was in his arms, nothing else mattered. I didn't care if we were found . . . if Father knew we were together. Now?' Natália buried her face in her hands with a cry of distress. 'I know he won't believe a word I say. Downstairs, he looked at me as if he hated me.'

'That is because you have injured his pride. I told you he was a real man. This is not his way. I have spoken with his men . . . Do you know what they call your Major Sorrell? "*El León*—the Lion." A king among men —and among women, so they say. He can have his pick of any one he likes, wherever he goes. They have only to hear of his courage and his leadership and, of course, the fact that he comes from a very wealthy family, to flock around him in dozens. He does not need your father's *quinta, menina*, or the promise of land for his children. He has all these things, and more.'

'And now he has a wife he does not want,' Natália returned miserably. 'He told me he had no intention of marrying.'

'Make him want you. Here, put this on.' Pilar had gone to a large mahogany chest at the bottom of the bed and pulled from it a nightgown and matching robe in pastel blue muslin. 'It will not be wasted on this one, believe me,' she added, as Natália hesitated. It was part of the trousseau intended for her marriage to Cesar.

Natália allowed her to draw off the velvet robe she wore and replace it with the blue. The sheerness of the material left very little to the imagination, and she quickly slipped the robe over the nightgown, fastening the dark blue ribbons across her exposed breasts.

'Look at yourself,' Pilar urged gently. 'Believe in yourself—in your love. Show him. He is only a man, not a stone statue!'

'No, he is not that,' Natália thought, lifting her eyes to stare at her reflection. Neither of them was made of stone. As she considered herself, she resolved that she had nothing to lose by showing Adam her willingness to accept him as her husband. If they could only capture those wonderful moments they had shared tonight and continue from there! She would not allow happiness to slip through her fingers. She would fight for it—and for him!

Pilar smiled to herself as Natália ran her fingers through her loose hair, deliberately arranging it about her shoulders. The blue matched her eyes, and the soft candlelight which filled the room enhanced the alabaster skin. He was a fool if he did not want her, the woman thought, and from what she had heard of Adam Sorrell, he was certainly not that!

When Adam came into the room, Natália was standing near the bed, looking across at the double set of pillows now arranged there and the silk sheets which had been turned back before Pilar left her only moments before. She did not seem to hear him come in, and he quietly closed the door behind him and turned the key in the lock before depositing the tray he carried on the dressing-table.

At the sound of a champagne-cork popping, Natália turned with a soft gasp. He moved with the stealth of a jungle animal, she thought, as she steeled herself to meet his gaze. Tonight he was the hunter and she was the prey. He poured out two glasses of sparkling wine and held one out to her.

'Your father gave me a toast downstairs. To a joyful union. Shall we drink to that? Tomorrow the marriage will have been consummated, and your father's dream well on its way to becoming reality.' The quiet insolence was meant to hurt her, and it succeeded. He saw her hand was trembling as she took the glass and quickly swallowed the contents.

'Champagne, like a good wine and a beautiful woman, should never be hurried, but I don't suppose you know that. You don't know much about anything really, do you, Natália? You may have played your little games many times before with poor fools who fell head over heels for those bewitching blue eyes, but never with a real man.'

Adam refilled her glass, and lifted it towards her lips when she hesitated. He was in a bitter, vengeful mood which he had not allowed himself to acknowledge throughout the brief ceremony, nor afterwards, as he stood listening to Dom Abílio sing his daughter's praises: how obedient she would be . . . a perfect hostess to grace his table and entertain his friends . . . a loving mother for the many children they would have. He had closed his ears to it all and drunk glass after glass of mellowed brandy until it was time to go upstairs to his bride. He was far from drunk, but he was dangerous.

He would give them both what they wanted. Natália would have a husband—for one night only—and from that, he had no doubt, the old man would receive his grandson. Once he left the *quinta*, he never wanted to see or hear of either of them again. He tried not to look at Natália, but he could not help himself. She was making things easier for him by looking so lovely. He stared rudely at the outline of breasts and thighs against the flimsy material, and reminded himself of the ugliness and treachery that lay beneath the outward beauty. She was a liar and a trickster who was about to have the tables turned on her.

'The bride is radiant!' He smiled as he put down his empty glass, took hers and put it aside.

'Adão, please listen to me? You must!' Natália entreated as he stepped towards her. There was a coldness about him which made her very afraid. He was going to make love to her because her father expected it. Shame swept over her, brought colour rushing to her cheeks. His fingers brushed her arm, continued up to her shoulder, tracing the path of the ribbons to where they rested in a bow between her breasts. He unfastened them and drew away the wrap. It slid to the floor and lay in a pool of pale froth about her ankles. 'I did not want this! You must believe me.'

'Very well, I believe you.' His tone indicated that he did not. She tried to ignore the fingers moving slowly over her bare skin, caressing her breasts beneath the nightgown. His touch burned her like fire.

'I love you. I do! I have never loved Cesar. I hated everything about him. Tonight has shown you the kind of man he is!'

'I should say you are well matched,' Adam replied indifferently. Long golden lashes swept down over eyes welling with tears. She really was amazing, he thought, slipping an arm round her waist to pull her closer. She had been caught out in lies and intrigue, yet still she protested that she loved him. Was one man more or less the same for her? Had she no shame? No pride?

'Please don't be cruel! Let me tell you the truth?' Natália begged. This was not going as she had planned. Pilar had been so sure that, once he saw her looking so seductive, he would fall into her arms and forget the unpleasantness between them. He was using her to soothe his wounded vanity, just as he would have used her in the orchard for his pleasure . . . and she would have let him! She bit her lip and was silent.

'Why stop now?' he taunted. 'Why not continue this farce to the very end?'

'I've told you I did not intend it to go as far as this,' she whispered pitifully. 'I—I have never known a man like you before . . . never known love . . . I am not alone at fault. You wanted me! You kissed me.'

'That was something we both wanted . . . as this is,' Adam growled, pressing his mouth to hers in a fierce, passionate kiss that left her breathless. Abruptly releasing her, he began to unfasten the front of his shirt. Natália stood frozen as he pulled it off, revealing a bronzed chest dark with hair. A scar criss-crossed the left shoulder. A mirthless smile tugged at his lips as he sat on the edge of the bed and tugged off his boots. 'You look a trifle pale, my dear. Surely you have seen a man undress before?'

'No.' She forced the word through stiff lips. 'There is a

dressing-room over there. Dona Margarida used to sleep there. Use that!'

'And she has no use for it, now that you have a new watchdog?' he chuckled. 'No more have I! The whole object of the exercise was to get yourself a husband, wasn't it? You succeeded. Much good it will do you.'

'I never wanted to be married. Not to Cesar . . . and certainly not to you.' She flung the words at him bitterly. How dare he humiliate her in this way!

Adam leaned back on his elbows and surveyed the indignant face. 'Come here, my wife,' he ordered. 'Now.'

It was not a request, but a command, and she regretted the instinctive response which made her obey and sink down beside him on the bed-covers. As he rose above her, she quailed at the glittering eyes, and shivered as he slipped the nightgown over her head and tossed it away, while she sought to make him listen to her once again. She reached up and covered his lips with her fingers as his head bent towards hers, whispering softly,

'Hold me as you did tonight when we talked of the lonely princess and the prince who loved her. Weave the same spell, so that it can be as it was then. Let me show you how much I love you . . . It is the only way I can make you believe, my husband of little faith.'

It was she who lifted herself and laid her mouth against his, entwining her arms about his neck and bringing him hard against her. She felt him stiffen as he fought to resist her and the inviting body straining against his . . . fought and lost, and returned her kiss with a hungry ardour that sent her senses spinning.

He laid bare her soul with caresses that brought tiny cries of delight to her lips. She murmured his name as his mouth took hers by storm and then left it, to devastate her body. She had won! The sweet joy which rose inside her swept aside all inhibitions . . . all doubts . . .

'Oh, Adão, we shall have such fine children!' she

breathed, 'I shall give you strong sons, just like their father . . .'

It took a moment for it to register that Adam was no longer kissing her . . . not even holding her. Her eyes flew open in alarm. What had she said? Done? He was standing by the bed, looking down at her, and she recoiled from the sardonic smile that masked his features.

'There will be no children, Natália. Ever. I am not going to touch you. Look elsewhere to give your father his precious grandson.'

'What—what are you saying?' As his eyes raked over her naked loveliness, she realised how he had tricked her. Deliberately he had set out to rouse her and had succeeded . . . To hurt her! To wound her! She wanted to strike him, but was too stunned by such callousness to move, or to defend herself against the unjust accusations flung at her.

'You have nothing to offer me. You are a child playing at being a woman. That may have suited the others, but I am more selective. I would rather pay for my pleasures than bed you!'

Snatching up his clothes, he turned and disappeared into the dressing-room. Natália heard the key turn in the lock, but it was some time before she managed to lift herself and crawl beneath the sheets, hugging them round her as if afraid he might return and tear them from her and demand his rights. She huddled beneath them, shivering violently, even though every part of her body burned from his touch.

As the hours slipped past, she accepted that he was not coming back. She would never be his wife! He had been forced to marry her, and had given her his name, but that was all she would have. Tears soaked the pillow beneath her cheek. She tried to hold them back, but they engulfed her like a tidal wave. He had rejected her love, treated her with less consideration than he would a paid prostitute! She rocked to and fro in silent agony, overcome with shame and self-pity—the next moment hating him! Reproaching herself and then blaming him for that first kiss! If only he had never touched her . . . What was the use!

How would she face her father and Alída in the morning? She could not tell them the truth. What could she do? Where could she go? She could not stay at the *quinta* and have her father watching her every day, waiting for the first sign of pregnancy . . . That was how it would be! Shame, and more shame, bitter retribution for her own folly. The tears would not cease. She buried her face in the silken pillows so that no sound carried to the room beyond.

CHAPTER SIX

ADAM TOOK a last look round the small room where his belongings had been left during his stay at Alto Verde, to make sure that everything had been replaced in his saddlebags and on the pack-horse, although he knew that when Nuno cleared up after him, not a thing would be overlooked. Then he moved out into the early morning sunlight which was weakly trying to force its way through dense white clouds, buttoning his leather jacket about him as he did so. He was dressed casually for the journey home in well-worn hide breeches, his head covered against the penetrating sun he knew to expect about noon.

From beneath the wide-brimmed black hat, narrowed eyes bleakly swept upwards for a brief moment, surveying the upstairs windows of the house he had left at first light. Like a silent spectre he had slipped out of the dressing-room as soon as he was able to see clearly without lighting a candle, dressed, and unlocked the door to Natália's bedroom. Why had he locked it, he wondered with grim amusement? Against her—or against the resentment he harboured that might have sent him back to finish what he had started? To satisfy the desire to wound, to inflict pain such as he had endured these past hours, or to recapture the bliss of those stolen moments in the orchard? Never would he feel that way again with any woman. He would ensure that. What a fool he had been to act like an idiotic schoolboy over a trollop! 'With the looks of an angel' was his next thought, as he paused beside the bed. Natália lay on her side facing him, one arm tucked beneath her head. The long tousled curls lay in profusion over the pillow; some shadowed her face, hiding it from him—and the deathly pallor which lay upon her cheeks. Soft, full lips were parted slightly. He remembered their softness, their eagerness, when his own had touched them. God! What had she done to him?

A few yards away, his men were quietening their restless horses. He ignored their glances, and a scowling countenance was turned in the direction of one man foolish enough to ask laughingly how the groom was. He peered through the half-light at the two figures approaching, and the heavy frown returned at the sight of Drew and Alída. The girl was enveloped in a thick travelling cloak which covered her from head to toe. Not that there would be anyone to see them depart, he thought. After last night and the abundance of wine that had flowed well into the early hours, there would be no early risers. By the time the village began to stir, they would be miles away. Then, perhaps, the tight restriction in his chest would begin to ease.

'You're late,' he said ungraciously, tucking the pistol Nuno handed him into the wide leather belt about his waist. Although in friendly territory, he was always armed. Nestled in his boot was a long-bladed knife, as deadly as his ability to use it. Every one of his men, with the exception of his brother, was skilled in the bloody art of silent warfare which had taught them to creep up behind a man and slit his throat before he could utter a sound. Not his favourite weapon, but silent and effective. He preferred the curved cavalry sabre that hung at his side. 'I said first light!'

'You may not have slept, brother, but I did,' Drew drawled mildly. 'I take it that you did not have a—pleasant wedding night?'

'That's none of your business! We are ready to leave. I hope you are a good horsewoman, senhora? I set a fast pace. I want to put this place behind me as quickly as possible.'

'And my sister?' Alída said, staring up into the grim features. What had taken place to make him look so devilishly angry? The few brief minutes she had spent with Natália after the ceremony had been spent in trying to persuade her sister to accept the marriage and the husband forced on her. 'Is it your intention to leave her behind now? When will she be following us to Lisboa?'

'Never,' Adam snapped, swinging himself into the saddle of his black horse. 'Natália and I will never set eyes on each other again . . .'

Over the loud gasp which came from Alída's lips, he heard his brother murmur, 'Wrong . . . look!'

He could not believe the sight that met his eyes. Hair streaming down her back . . . He had not realised how long it was, falling to her waist, and even in the faint sunlight, he could see strands of fire among the gold. Natalia was running towards them. She was clutching a wrap round her, yet it did little to hide the transparencey of the garment beneath. Her feet were bare, as though she had departed from her bed in great haste. She must have seen them from her window, he realised, and cursed his brother for not being on time. The delay would cost them all dear.

'The bride is not anxious to be left alone,' Drew said, stepping back to allow her to come close to Adam.

Adam stepped closer as she approached, to prevent her being beside her sister when he spoke to her. What he had to say was for her ears alone.

'I told you last night how it would be between us,' he hissed. 'Why do you make a spectacle of yourself in this fashion? *No tens vergonha?*'

'No, I have no shame,' Natália flung back, her voice low to match his. Her sapphire eyes were without tears, and in the depths of them he saw fire—brilliant blue sparks of anger only just controlled. 'Nor pride. You have left me neither! I have come to say goodbye to my sister.'

Brushing past him, she took Alída in her arms, and she could feel Natália trembling. With cold, was her first instinctive thought, then, as she drew back and looked into Natália's eyes, she knew differently.

'What is it? What has happened? He—he was not unkind?'

'No, he was not that,' came the toneless reply. She would not spoil her sister's departure with her own troubles. She was a married woman now, in control of her life, for the first time in seventeen years. With Cesar, it would have been different. He would never have allowed her one iota of freedom, but Adam had *given* her hers! She would make the most of it. What did she care if he went off and left her? 'I shall come and see you in a little while.'

'But of course you will, and then you can tell me what this is all about.'

'It's nothing. I am being foolish. A nervous bride,' Natália returned with forced lightness. She was aware of Adam straining his ears to catch some word and deliberately leaned closer to Alída, whispering, as she kissed a cheek chilled by the early morning air, 'Soon, I promise. I shall dance at your wedding.'

'If Father allows you to come! If not, I shall expect you in Mafra. Drew thinks he will be posted back there after Lisboa. Adam, too. You are a soldier's wife now, and must go where your husband goes. I intend to follow Drew no matter where he is sent. I could not bear to be parted from him.'

'You will be happy this time, I know it,' Natália said, and her heart ached for the love she knew she must deny herself. She looked at the silent man watching them. Adam's face betrayed no expression, yet something about him made her uneasy.

She kissed and hugged her sister one last time, loath to let her go, but it would not be for long. It was her intention to follow Adam to Lisboa—he could not stop her if she chose to do so. She would make some excuse and stay with Alída, and somehow she would make him pay for the humiliation he had heaped on her head, his cruel refusal to listen to her declaration of love, the vile accusations that she had known other men. He had only to touch her to discover otherwise!

There was her answer! She *would* go to Lisboa. He could not deny her as his wife, especially if she made herself known to his father as if she were expected! He would have to acknowledge her . . . to share the same room, or risk everyone knowing what he had done to her!

Drew helped Alída to mount. She reached down from the saddle and clung to Natália's hand, her pretty face distressed.

'I hate to leave you alone, but if I do not go now with Drew . . . Come as soon as you can, and try to bring Father with you. He will be lonely with us both absent. Be kind to him, Natália. We shall have our happiness, but he will have nothing—no one—if we turn our backs on him now. We can be generous.'

Lonely. Yes, he was that, Natália acknowledged. So was she, but they would not be able to share their troubles. They would never be that close.

As she turned away, without a word to her husband, he caught her arm, bringing her to an abrupt halt.

'Take the men and ride on,' he said to his brother. 'I'll catch up with you in a few minutes. I must say goodbye to my wife.'

A thickset Spaniard paused beside them as the rest of the twenty grinning men passed by, knowing they must resist the urge to turn and watch what they considered to be an ardent farewell on the part of their commanding officer or risk their sergeant's leather whip across their shoulders. Adam jerked his head, and the man nodded and rode on. Nuno, the last to ride out, paused and waited.

'I shall wait for you, *chefe*,' he said, and dark eyes glared at Natália with unconcealed venom. He disliked her. She had tricked his beloved master into a loveless marriage, and his animosity knew no bounds. He hoped she was cursed by the saints for the harm she had done, the pain she had brought to a good and kind man. In his way, he was as protective about Adam as Pilar was for her mistress.

'No, join the others. I will be a moment only,' Adam ordered. The boy nodded. He knew better than to disobey a direct order. His back stiff with anger, he slowly rode after the *guerrilleros*.

'If you have any ideas about following me to Lisboa, forget them,' he said flatly, and Natália started so violently that he knew he had been right. 'Stay out of Alída's life . . . Your troubles are not hers. You brought them on yourself, and you must pay the penalty. She and Drew will be married soon. Don't come to the wedding.'

'She is my sister. I shall do as I please,' Natália snapped, defiance blazing out of her pale face. How dare he treat me like one of his cut-throat men! 'As your wife, I have rights . . .'

She cried out as he seized her by the shoulders, his fingers biting cruelly through the thin material of her robe. His face came close to hers, and she quailed at the fury registered in his tawny eyes. He shook her just once, hard, then thrust her away from him.

'It is my dearest wish never to set eyes on you again! In Lisboa I shall make arrangements to have the marriage annulled. If you are sensible, it will be done quietly and discreetly. In time, the dowry your father so generously gave me will be returned. I want nothing to remind me of you or my visit to this accursed village. But if you give me any trouble'—his voice dropped to a threatening low —'I shall see your name dragged in the gutter where you rightfully belong! It is up to you. I shall not wish you luck in your search for a husband to provide your father with his heir. I am sure you will not need it.'

She swayed back from him, her eyes dilated in disbelief. Adam swung himself into the saddle and wheeled the stallion about without another word. Red dust rose up in a cloud to choke her as he kneed the animal away at a furious pace, and within minutes they were lost to view among the meandering houses. He had gone! She was alone! Alone for ever!

A mile out of Alto Verde on the road to Lisboa, Alída reined in her horse, her face a mask of indecision 'I'm going back. I can't leave her alone like this,' she declared, as Drew swung his horse in beside her.

'Do you know what you are saying? We shall have little enough time together as it is. Are you prepared to jeopardise our happiness because your sister acted like a damned fool?'

'I know that neither you nor Adam believe she meant no harm, but I know differently. She loves him, Drew. As deeply as I love you. I shall never forget the look on her face as we left—never! Your brother is a cruel man. I don't know what he said to her, but he hurt her deeply. She needs me.'

Ahead of them, Adam reined in and turned to stare back curiously as Drew retorted sharply,

'I need you, too. I want to spend every moment with you. Besides, my father is expecting to meet you. I have already sent word ahead that we are coming.'

'You didn't tell me!' Alída gasped. 'Oh, Drew, I want to help her, but I don't know how. You wouldn't desert Adam if he needed you.'

'No, but this is a quite different situation from anything we shall ever encounter,' he told her quietly. He understood her fears, but accepted that neither of them could help Natália for the moment. Not that he particularly wanted to. If he offered a hand in friendship again, it would be for Alída's sake only. He stood with Adam in this.

'She and Adam must work this out together, painful as it is for both of us . . . Yes, dear heart, both of us. We must give them time. A few weeks' separation may bring them to their senses.'

'She did say she would soon come to Mafra.' Alída was beginning to waver. She had so much been looking forward to being alone with the man she loved. Making plans for this wedding would be very different from the last time. 'But Adam said . . .'

'I'll deal with my brother if he's difficult,' Drew assured her, kissing her lightly on the lips. How, he did not know. No one, not even their father, could handle Adam when he dug his heels in.

'What was that all about?' demanded Adam, as Alída passed him and Drew came level, slowing the pace of his horse to enable them to converse. When he was told, his face darkened with anger. 'Don't try to back me into a corner. I told you how it was going to be. The marriage will be annulled as soon as possible. This is between us, you understand? There is no need for Alída to know until the sordid business has been dealt with.'

'She was hoping . . . after you had been apart for a while, perhaps . . . well, you know.'

'Nothing has happened between Natália and myself. Nor will it,' Adam returned coldly. 'I shall never acknowledge her as my wife, and I shall be rid of her at the first available opportunity. Is that clear enough for you?'

'Alída wants her to come to Mafra.'

'That's up to her. So long as she doesn't expect me to be there if and when Natália arrives. Don't let her influence you over this, Drew, or your marriage will be wrecked before it's started. If you have anything worth while—then hold on to it,' he added with heavy sarcasm, indicating to his brother that he still did not think Alída capable of being faithful to one man.

'Just because life has turned sour on you, Adam, that doesn't mean we all have to suffer,' Drew snapped, and Adam blinked at him in surprise.

'You are right. Perhaps they are not alike. I'm sorry . . . I didn't sleep very well . . .' He balked at confiding to his brother his conduct of the night before. He was not proud of himself, even though he repeatedly told himself that Natália had deserved no better. A lesser man might have used her to satisfy the pain and anger, to render hurt for hurt, and then leave, but he could not have done that. He will still asking himself why!

'Let's ride,' he said gruffly.

'I have had a letter from Alída, Father. Drew has been ordered back to Mafra, as she thought. They leave Lisboa at the end of this week,' Natália announced to the man sitting at the far end of the long table, engrossed in a paper. Headlines blazed the advance of French troops towards the Linhas de Torres Vedras, where the English army was encamped within forts and earthworks, their cannon trained upon the distant hills of Monte Agraço where Musséna had his vanguard, sweeping the country-side from behind inpenetrable defences from coast to coast in an attempt to stave off all chance of the enemy reaching the capital.

After a moment, Abílio lifted his eyes, allowing himself the pleasure of studying her as she returned her attention to the letter in her hand. A hundred times he had tried to ask her what was wrong, but the words never materialised, and instead he found himself chiding her time and time again, as the weeks passed, for not going to her husband.

Natália's hair was loose about her shoulders, framing a pale but serene face. She wore a green skirt—her mother's favourite colour, he remembered—and a lighter blouse which fastened high under the slender neck with three rows of tiny pearl buttons. Her countenance gave him no cause to believe all was not well with her marriage. She had said that when she had made adequate preparations she would join Adam Sorrell, but she wanted to take so many things with her to grace her new home, wherever it might be. Was she pleased with the man she had chosen, he wondered, but he dared not ask for fear she misconstrued his meaning.

'I too, have heard from your sister. I am surprised, however, to have recieved nothing from Major Sorrell. Neither have you, I see. I thought at least an apology was in order for the swiftness of his departure before I was even out of my bed.'

'I have told you, Father. He is not a man to prolong a parting. We had been together only a few hours. He did not want to leave so soon, but he had his orders.'

'He found time to linger at Alto Verde . . . and dally with you!' Abílio broke off as a cloud crossed her face.

'Has Alída asked you to visit her in Mafra? I think I shall go, and you should, too. It is time you got to know your son-in-law, as you were not well enough to go to their wedding. Let there be peace between us all. After all, you have doubled your chances of having a grandson, have you not?'

Like him, she could not keep the sarcasm from her remarks. Would there never be a time when they were at ease together? She had come to desire it more and more since Alída left. Sometimes the urge to confide in him was so overwhelming that she found herself actually beginning to blurt out a full explanation . . . only quickly to curb the impulsive words and turn away. He would not go to Mafra, of course. He rarely went outside the *quinta* these days, but when she had asked if he was ill and perhaps she should send for the doctor, he had waved aside the idea.

This was a heaven-sent opportunity for her to see her sister again—and Adam. He could not prevent her from visiting Mafra and staying at her sister's house. In her letter, Alída had made it quite plain she thought Natália had lingered long enough in Alto Verde. She was to come as soon as possible, she wrote, and she would arrange for Adam to be at the house upon her arrival.

'Let us hope I do not have to wait much longer, then,' Dom Abílio said, rising to his feet.

What it was to be young and in love. New confidence had grown in her since her marriage . . . Once, before life's disappointments had soured him and the only woman he had ever loved had been taken from him, he, too, had felt that way. Natália's performance was so impeccable that he never guessed the agony of mind she experienced each night as she tossed and turned restlessly on her empty marriage bed. Each morning she greeted him smilingly at breakfast and then rode for hours alone in the surrounding countryside as she had always done. In the afternoons she would ponder over the enormous list she had drawn up, as if unable to make up her mind what articles of furniture she wished to take with her —what clothes, draperies and linen.

Abílio paused beside her chair, his eyes once more centred on the paper he held. After a moment he dropped it in front of her.

'From the news here, it seems Viscount Wellington is soon to launch a new campaign to end this wretched war. You will have little enough time to spend with your husband. Will you return here if he goes into Spain?'

'I—I don't know. I hadn't thought so far ahead. I might remain with Alída.'

'When your men go off to war, you must return here—both of you—where I can take care of you. They will expect it of me.'

His words struck deep into Natália's heart. He looked very old, suddenly, and his hair seemed greyer than usual this morning, his face more drawn. Or was it just a trick of the light? He had eaten very little again. Perhaps she should send for the doctor without his knowledge. She was no longer angry with him. He had asked her if Adam was her choice of man, and when she had said he was, he had given him to her. Just like that! Now it was up to her to fight her way back into the affections of the man who had deserted her.

'Of course,' she said, understanding. He wanted to be the first to know if there was a child on the way. Poor Father, in her case he might not live to see the day. 'We shall both come back in the summer. You know how unpleasant the city is then,' she added, hoping to offer a crumb of comfort to the father who had never given her comfort or love and yet who, as she stared at him, roused compassion in her. They had shared none of the things they should, avoided each other's company whenever possible . . . Yet now, at this moment of parting, something inexplicable reached out to touch her heart.

That evening, as she was about to retire, the sound of a carriage drawing up in the courtyard outside drew her to the window, fearing Cesar might have returned to create another unpleasant scene before her departure. The man who alighted was a stranger to her. Powerfully built, with rugged features illuminated by the patio lights and a shock of red hair.

'Do you know him?' she asked Pilar, and the woman shook her head. 'What a time to come calling, too! It is almost eleven o'clock. Does he not remind you of anyone?'

'*Não, menina.* I am sure we have never seen him before. Into bed with you now, we have an early start in the morning. You are set on going to him?'

'Nothing will change my mind. At first I was full of bitterness and anger,' Natália confessed. 'I intended to make him fall in love with me'—she gave a shaky little laugh as she pondered the enormous undertaking—'and then desert *him*! But I know now I cannot do that.

Perhaps he will have forgiven me, and we can start again. I shall pray it is so.'

Natália had barely started on her devotions before the small shrine of the Virgin in a corner of the room, when a servant knocked on the door with a message from her father requesting her to come downstairs.

As she appeared in the doorway of the library, a heavy velvet robe covering her night attire, the stranger turned to stare at her. As his eyes alighted on her, to sweep her from head to toe, she realised why he had seemed so familiar. The same boldness as he scrutinised her in silence, the same way as Adam had looked at her that very first night. It had to be his father! But here at the *quinta*? Why? Something had happened to him? She choked back the fear which rose inside her as the man crossed the room to take her in his arms and subject her to a fierce bear-hug that squeezed the breath from her body.

'Natália! It has to be. And more lovely than my son's description of you. A veritable picture of loveliness, he said, and how right he is,' a voice boomed in her ear. Adam's words! She was too astounded to speak. 'I am on my way to Mafra to visit an old friend, and I thought —why not get acquainted with my new daughter-in-law before she rushes off to be with her husband? You are joining him there, are you not?'

'Why—yes, of course.' From the smile on her father's face, she saw he was pleased at this show of affection. Any fears he might have harboured were laid to rest.

'Natália, this is Adam's father, Senhor Charles Sorrell. What a blessing his arrival could turn out to be . . . you could travel with him. You would not mind acting as my daughter's chaperon, would you, senhor?'

'It would be my pleasure.'

'You are too kind, but I could not trouble you . . .' Natália began, then the words froze in her throat as she realised the newcomer was watching her closely. Something was not right. Adam had never used such words to describe her . . . if he *had* spoken of her at all to his father. Of that she was sure. If he had forgiven her, he would have come himself. This man had come to inspect her, she decided, and to determine whether or not she was a fit wife for his son. What had he been told?

She met his gaze with level, challenging blue eyes and saw a smile touch the full mouth. A silent acknowledgment of the fact that she knew his reasons for stopping at Alto Verde.

'If you can be ready in the morning, we can leave early,' Charles Sorrell murmured. 'Once you are settled —I expect Adam will find a house soon—you can send for your things. I expect you are anxious to be with him again and don't want to linger over packing. My son's duties have kept him busy these past few weeks. Not his fault, of course, but he was afraid you might think him an unfeeling brute for not coming himself. He has new orders, from Lord Wellington himself. What they are he has not told me, but I expect they will take him into the thick of the fighting when it starts again. Adam enjoys a fight. We are alike in that way. Now Drew is not at all like either of us . . .' He broke off with a soft laugh. 'But I will not bore you with talk of our shortcomings; if we are to make an early start, you should get a good night's rest. On the way I shall want to hear how you captured Adam's heart in such a short space of time. The man is so enamoured of you that I can hardly believe it. I despaired of him ever settling down! You will give him a strong, healthy son! Will she not, Senhor Lareira?'

'I pray she does—for us both,' Abílio replied, and this time Charles laughed heartily.

'If I know my son, she will have an army of youngsters!'

Abílio did not reply, but Natália noticed his smile deepen in satisfaction. Was she no more than a breeding mare to be discussed in this manner? Men! That's all they thought about.

'It is late, and I was about to retire when you arrived,' she said politely, but with a touch of ice in her voice that did not go unnoticed by either man. 'Please excuse me, senhor. Father. I shall see you both in the morning.'

'Of course, my dear.' Again the same tight hug; the lips laid to each cheek—not without some warmth, she realised. The man was genuinely pleased to have met her. What had Adam told him? Or Alída? Her sister, knowing how she felt, could not have kept silent in the face of Adam's refusal to accept her as his wife. Had she pleaded Natália's cause?

It was barely nine when Natália found herself standing in the hall, fumbling for words as she faced her father. Would he miss his daughters, she wondered, as he muttered something about a safe journey, and patted her hand. Why, oh why had he never taken more time to know them? They were his own flesh and blood. She tried, but could not bring herself, to kiss the proffered cheek.

'I shall be back before you know it,' she said, forcing a smile to her lips. It was what he wanted to hear, after all.

'Will you?' The harshness of tone took her aback. Emotion choked the usually calm voice, and she watched him fight to control it. 'Will you and your sister ever return here, Natálinha?'

Little Natália! He had not used that term of endearment with her since she became old enough to understand it. Now, of all times, to remind her! She could not prevent the bright tears which sprang to her eyes.

'*Sim, pai.* We shall come back. I promise.' The words came unbidden to her lips.

She turned to go, and found his hand was on her arm. He drew her to him, held her for a moment, looking deep into her blue eyes, before kissing her on both cheeks. The show of affection added to the sense of puzzlement and apprehension she was experiencing at this strange departure. The arrival of Adam's father had shocked her beyond words. Now her own father was actually being kind to her and not caring who witnessed the scene. Charles Sorrell had already gone out to the carriage, but the hall contained all the servants waiting to bid her farewell. Pilar's face, as she stood waiting for her mistress by the door, was a picture of amazement.

Abílio followed her to the door, but no further. She lifted a hand in a farewell salute as the conveyance moved off. Villagers were crowding about the gate, shouting their good wishes for the new bride and the one yet to be, but she scarcely saw them. She could not take her eyes off the solitary figure who stood in the doorway watching, his arm raised . . .

As the dust began to settle on the roadway, Abílio realised that people were drifting away, glancing at him with sympathetic faces as they passed, until he was alone on the steps. The pain struck again, searing through his chest with the viciousness of a red-hot knife. He stumbled into the study, locked the door so that no servants could disturb him, and poured himself a large glass of wine. He drank it quickly and sank into a chair. Gradually it died, leaving him weak and trembling . . . unable to move . . .

Charles Sorrell crossed one booted leg over the other, glanced at Pilar who was looking out of the window at the passing landscape and intermittently dozing, despite the rocking of the carriage, as though trying to make up his mind about something. A frown creased the heavy red brows as he directed his attention to the quiet, simply dressed young woman facing him. Her travelling gown of deep blue velvet enhanced the magnificent colour of her eyes. Perched on top of the copper curls was a bonnet of a darker colour, trimmed with ribbons which tied beneath her chin. Her gloves were of white goatskin, hand-made, he suspected by the villagers who adored her, as were the dainty leather shoes. Beside her on the seat was an embroidered reticule and a heavy shawl of black wool. If she had set out to make a good impression on him, she would have succeeded—except that he had come prepared to dislike her on sight. However, he had found that impossible. He liked what he saw, and understood the attraction his son must have felt at his first glimpse of this lovely creature.

'Does my appearance meet with your approval, sir?' Natália enquired politely. His scrutiny embarrassed her. His eyes were so like those of Adam—penetrating —allowing nothing to remain hidden. What had he talked about, closeted in the library with her father until well past four in the morning? How much had he been told?

'My son was right. You have the face of an angel and a sweet voice to charm the birds from the trees, but I'll tell you this now, young lady . . . you have turned a good-natured man into a veritable bear. Why, he even argues with me, his own father . . . and if it hadn't been for that sister of yours, I'd never have known why.'

'He . . . Adam never told you we are married?' Her words were barely audible. 'Then he did not send for me? I knew it!'

'You are his wife, and your place is with him. That's why I came to fetch you. He knows nothing about it. You'll just have to work things out when you are together. Your sister wants me to believe that would mean a great deal to you.'

'I love Adam. There is nothing more I want in this world than to be his wife, but . . .'

'But you acted like an idiot . . . If I'm to believe you care for him, that's what you were—and are—for expecting him to forgive you. Good heavens, girl, he's never loved a woman in his life before you . . . He's had women—what man, especially a soldier, has not!—but to think of taking a wife!' Charles's face grew quite red with indignation as he considered the pale features before him, the hands locked tightly together on the velvet skirts. He was not sure what he had expected her to say when he confronted her with the truth . . . He had been prepared for apologies . . . remorse . . . even lies, but she said nothing, and sat perfectly still, her back stiff and straight. He liked her for that and for the steady gaze of those eyes now filled with shadows. He never trusted anyone who would not look into his eyes.

'Adam's a hothead sometimes,' his voice was softer now, and gentler. 'You've hurt him, and he wants to pay you back.'

'He has, believe me,' Natália whispered. 'He—he rejected me on our wedding night.' A faint blush came to her cheeks with the humiliating admission. 'But I still love him. If he will have me . . .'

'He's talking of an annulment. I persuaded him to leave it until after Alída's wedding. In that way, I had a chance to get you to Mafra to face him. Your sister is very convincing.'

'She knows I have never loved any man before . . . Nor—nor been with one, as Adam accuses.'

'You've picked a jealous man to try to hold on to. Maybe you'll succeed—maybe not. If I have my way, you will. I don't know why, but I think you'd be good for him. He's been alone too long . . . He needs other things in his life besides ambitious dreams . . .'

'I had dreams once,' Natália broke in, not minding the roughness of his speech when he talked with her. He was an honest man, she decided, who dearly loved his son. Perhaps, together . . . 'Adam is the answer to mine. If he will allow it, I shall try to make his come true. I swear it! Somehow!'

'Are you prepared to go through hell for him, because if I know my son, that's exactly where he'll take you until he's sure of you?' Charles demanded.

'I shall pay any price to have him . . . do anything . . . go anywhere!' she cried, and Charles drew in a breath at the change in her. Gone were the docility and meek manners. There was fire in her eyes and a stubborn jutting of the well-defined chin. Determination in the tightening of the soft mouth. Did his son fully understand what he had left behind, he wondered, as he settled back in his seat? A woman of spirit to match his own independent temperament. It would be a battle of wills between them, and one he hoped he would lose. This girl held Adam's happiness in her hands, and he was now ready to concede that she did love him. He was a good judge of character. Many years at the side of his sea-captain father had trained him well for the day he set foot ashore to stay and settle down in the land he had come to love and in which to go into business for himself. And had taught him to assess whether a person was trustworthy or not.

Adam shared his love of the sea and his shrewd mind for business, as well as inheriting a fatal charm which seemed to attract every pretty woman he encountered. His determination to remain a bachelor, until he had accomplished more in his life, only increased their desire to know him, to snare him and the tidy sum of money already in his possession. Addle-brained little simpering idiots, he mused, once again concentrating on the silent girl opposite. She had more backbone than all of them put together. A pity his son had been too blind with anger and bitter recriminations to see what lay under his nose.

Natália, increasingly aware of his gaze on her, kept her own averted, intent on the countryside, and so did not see the frown which returned to crease his brows. Did she know that her father was seriously ill? he wondered. There was a coldness between them he did not understand, even though Alída had told him of her father's indifference and total lack of affection. The girls were both to be highly prized as wives, yet Dom Abílio had seemingly thrust them both off on to men who cared not a whit for their feelings. He harboured a deep resentment within him. Charles had felt it as they talked into the early hours. He had seen the attack which seized Abílio and rendered him helpless—incapable of movement or speech—for several frightening minutes. And when it passed, he had found himself swearing an oath to remain silent as to what he had seen.

No wonder Natália had reached out with both hands to grab what she believed to be the reality of her dreams. Perhaps Adam would relent when he saw her again, listen to reason, give the marriage a chance. If he was not besotted with the girl, why had he been drunk for the best part of his leave, resuming an affair with an old flame and shirking the responsibilities he had once taken so seriously? Besotted—or so enamoured of her that he was afraid of his own feelings? Would not admit, even if she were the cheat he believed—and Charles, who had enjoyed more than his fair share of lovely beauties in his time, believed otherwise and intended to say so—that he still wanted her! Perhaps even loved her. Of course. Why had he not realised it before? Adam was in love! Charles began to grow restless as the miles rolled by, impatient to see his son's face when his wife alighted from the carriage.

Natália began to grow anxious at the signs of increased activity along the road to Mafra. More uniformed men marched back towards the Linhas de Torres Vedras with full packs and shouldered muskets. They passed cannon drawn by mule teams, mounted Dragoons in blue and red uniforms and cylindrical shakos, their breastplates and weapons gleaming in the sun. What a fine sight they looked, she thought. Surely one sight of them must put the French to flight?

Charles Sorrell pointed out the King's Own Regiment, or 4th Foot, in bright red coats and black and white breeches. The 9th Foot were known throughout Spain as the 'Holy Boys' because the crest of Britannia worn on their hats had been mistaken for that of the Virgin Mary. She prayed the mistake would keep them all safe, but she doubted it. A small contingent of kilted Highlanders stood to one side of the road watching the carriage go by, then started off again, led by their piper playing a stirring tune to keep their spirits up. As she watched the red and white tartan stockings disappear from view, her heart began to grow heavy. Her father had been right—there was about to be another offensive—and Adam was sure to be in the thick of it.

Somehow she contained her fears, and managed to sit still and calm as they laboured slowly through the crowded streets of Mafra, where more British uniforms jostled shoulder to shoulder with Spanish infantry and yellow-coated Spanish Dragoons. Charles watched her eyes grow more and more shadowed as the journey neared its end, but could say nothing to ease her apprehension. He had lingered too long before setting out for Alto Verde. If he had waited for Adam to tell him what was wrong, he would have waited for ever! Now it would be Natália who was forced to wait, to endure the agony of a long separation, the possibility that the husband she had never known would be killed. She was strong, she would survive—but she did not deserve such a harsh fate, and neither did his son!

He helped her to alight before an imposing house of white and grey stone, the residence left to Alída by her husband. The front was a mass of wrought-iron balustrades which reminded her of the *quinta*, and for a brief moment, she experienced a feeling of guilt. She had run away rather than tell her father the truth, that perhaps he would never have a grandchild—from her at least —and she did not like the way it made her feel. If only he had not looked so lonely and dejected as she left . . .

Then, her head lifting proudly, she thrust all thoughts,

save one, from her mind: the reason she had come to
Mafra. To confront Adam and *make* him accept her.
Charles rang the ornate brass bell hanging to one side of
the large oak door. Natália knew they would have to
wait several minutes for anyone to come. Alída had only
two servants, an aged housekeeper and her niece, and
neither was very quick on her feet. She managed a
patient smile, and Charles rang a second time. Was
Adam here? Had her sister managed to persuade him to
come to the house? But, of course, she would not know
of Natália's unexpected arrival . . . Better still if the
meeting was not planned. Adam was shrewd enough to
know Alída's desire to see them reunited.

The housekeeper at last swung back the massive
portal and they walked through into the pleasant courtyard which graced the front of the two-storeyed building. On one side were the servants' quarters and store-
house. On the other, a stable with the main living-
quarters above. Natália's steps faltered as they went up a
wide flight of steps, trying to answer the housekeeper's
enquiries as to her health and that of her father with a
relaxed smile on her face. By the time they reached the
long veranda that curved round the whole house, giving
access to all the upstairs room, she had to fight down a
rising panic.

She had eaten nothing at breakfast, and had drunk
only a glass of white wine when Charles suggested they
stop for refreshments *en route*. How she wished she had
been more sensible. Her stomach felt uncomfortably
hollow and her head quite light.

Sweet-smelling flowers were everywhere—lining the
pátio, the stairs, the balcony. Splashes of bright colour,
reds, mauves, brilliant scarlet and delicate pinks invaded
her eyes, and the air was heavy with the perfume of roses
and lilies. Alída always had had a magic way with
flowers. The cool of the drawing-room was most welcome after the heat of the carriage and the streets

outside. Although the nights were still cold, temperatures during the day had begun to soar as summer came to the countryside.

'Where is my sister, Maria Lopes?' Natália was beginning to think it strange that Alída had not appeared before now. The house seemed very quiet, the silence broken only by the sweet trilling of one of the caged canaries. 'Has she gone shopping? Is Captain Sorrell not here?'

'*Não*, Dona Natália . . . No one is here. They have gone.'

'Gone!' Charles exclaimed, as she sank down into a chair, her features so white that Pilar rushed to her side and began to fan her. 'Gone where? They could not have arrived more than four days ago!'

'To Sobral, senhor. It was very sudden. Major Sorrell and his brother received new orders, and left the same day. The senhora went with them.'

Adam had been at the house, and she had missed him! Was fate determined to snatch happiness from her grasp at every turn?

'There is a letter for you, Dona Natália. And if the senhor is Senhor Charles, then I have one for him also. I intended to send them when I went to the market in the morning. I will bring them,' she added, as Natália nodded.

'Thank heavens she's as slow in her ways as she is, or we would not know what is happening,' she said quietly.

'What will you do now?' Charles asked.

'That will depend on what news we receive.' Natália opened her letter in a feverish haste, unaware of Charles's interest. He saw her start, a slender hand flutter unsteadily to her lips. Crossing to where she sat, he plucked the paper from her lap where it had fallen unnoticed, and read it in silence.

'He does not want to see me,' Natália whispered. 'Alída writes there is no hope . . . ever! He is still intending to have the marriage annulled.'

'Over my dead body! The man has taken leave of his senses!' Charles read his own letter while she waited in an agony of suspense. 'Adam has been seconded to "special duties". By that, I take it to mean he's doing exactly what he was before with his Spanish *guerrilleros*. Only now, he says, he's also been asked to train Portuguese as well. Drew goes with him to take command of the cavalry screen which will monitor his activities and report back to their headquarters. They are at Sobral de Monte Agraço, my dear. It's not far.'

Not far. It could have been a thousand miles away, Natália thought. She had swallowed her fierce pride and followed him this far, but she could not go on. Her composure began to crumble in the face of this shattering new blow, and Charles's heart went out to her.

'I am sorry. I tried to talk him out of this annulment nonsense before he left Lisboa, but he is quite adamant. He tells me to proceed with it, and inform him when he is a free man.'

CHAPTER SEVEN

FOR DAYS Natália did not stir from the house, but remained closeted in her room with her grief and her shame. Charles often found her sitting beside the window, staring at the flower-strewn balcony, knowing she did not see a single bloom, that her mind was miles away in Sobral. He had made enquiries himself among the many army acquaintances he had in Mafra, but he had been unable to add very much to what they already knew.

Adam and his *guerrilleros* were operating in the countryside beyond Monte Agraço. Drew and his troop of cavalry were encamped on the slopes of the mountain itself, acting as a go-between. The latter were well within range of the cannon on the hillsides and were in no danger from a surprise attack, he assured her. Of Adam, he said nothing more, and Natália knew her husband was once more risking his life behind enemy lines with his highly-trained little group of men, reconnoitring the area, locating the French and assessing their strength, determining their course of action before he sketched his maps and sent them back to Sobral in the care of his brother. She inwardly shivered whenever she thought of the danger which must lurk all about him. The information had been given to him in the strictest confidence, Charles told her, and must not go beyond the house. She assured him that it would not.

He tried in vain to draw her out of her gloom, proposing rides together to enjoy the beautiful scenery that the town of Mafra offered. At last she gave in to his insistent pleas and agreed to take him on a sightseeing tour, for she had grown to know it well during the year after

Alída's husband had died, spending many weeks there after the funeral.

The town itself claimed the great distinction of being one of the oldest in Portugal, and one of the most fascinating with its ancient monastery of the same name situated on a near-by plateau. Built by Dom João V, the fulfilment of a vow that if God blessed him with a son after three fruitless years of marriage, he would erect a fine monument in His name—its mixture of Germanic, Italian and Portuguese architecture was set against a background of wheeling windmills. Later, when the immense structure began to attract many foreign artists, drawn to gaze in awe and admiration at the magnificent bells brought from Belgium and the Netherlands, the exquisite statues from Rome, the marble from Carrara, the king also had built the first school of sculpture, which in future years produced fine altar pieces and statues now to be found in the basilica.

Once Mafra had been a quiet little place where she had walked and ridden with her sister, shutting out all thoughts of her own approaching marriage. Now, it was a fortified town, she saw, as she reined in on a hill on the road leading northward. The second line of defence erected by Wellington's army stretched from the Rio Tejo, where gun batteries covering the estuary were set among thistles and rock roses, through Mafra to the Atlantic seaboard, where sheer cliffs made it impossible for the enemy to land. On the S-bend in the road ahead of her was one of the many forts guarding the way to Lisboa.

The town itself was a veritable fort with twenty redoubts and guns around the *tapada*—the Royal Park. Redoubts crossed scorched orange groves, twisted through olive and almond trees, over land that had once been covered with maize and crops of potatoes.

She was horrified by the devastation of the land by soldiers who claimed to be their friends and were trying

to deliver them from the menace of the French army, for
they had brought as much hardship to the people as did
the invaders. There was little enough food to provide for
the inhabitants already living inside the protection of the
lines, let alone those poor devils who had lost their
homes and been forced to seek shelter further south.
The additional mouths only produced more problems
and aroused fresh bitterness towards both sides. How
she prayed the war would soon end and that her lovely
country could once more flourish and grow, the wounds
heal and people return to the important task of reculti-
vating barren earth. How lucky were the people of Alto
Verde—and her father, whose vineyards were still
intact!

As Charles looked at her, Natália flicked away a
bright red dragonfly which insisted on hovering in front
of her nose, and turned her horse about.

'What will you do now?' Pilar stood at the end of the
bed, a frown on her usually placid features as she stared
at her mistress. The night before, Charles Sorrell had
announced he would be returning to Lisboa in two days.
They had been at the house for over two weeks, and
he could leave his business no longer. She knew that
Natália had spent another sleepless night after the announcement. 'Will you return with him, as he suggests?
Wait for Major Sorrell in Lisboa?'

'I might as well go home as do that. If only I could
reach Adam, and talk to him. Surely he could not refuse
to see me if I went to Sobral?'

'Could he not?' Pilar shrugged noncommittally. 'His
letter made it quite clear he does not want to see you
ever again.'

'I won't accept that!' Natália sprang out of bed, almost
upsetting the tray on the table beside her. She had
touched no breakfast, despite her maid's reproving comments. 'Why am I allowing myself to be treated like this?

I have done nothing wrong . . . He would treat a camp-follower better than he does me. Do you think he has a mistress, Pilar?'

The thought had been haunting her for days. Had Adam, in his anger and bitterness, taken another woman to give him solace? What would she do if he had? Oust the creature from his bed and demand her rights as his wife? In his eyes, she had none! There was only one course open to her, once she found him again. To ensure she was the only woman in his life—by whatever means at her disposal. But if she boldly arrived in Sobral and sought him out, he might well send her packing again, and shame her before his friends and colleagues.

Pilar took up a brush, and sitting her down, began to brush the long hair with loving strokes. Natália noticed that she did not answer the vital question. Instead, the maid said, 'I curse the day he ever came to Alto Verde! He is a fool, and not worthy of you. I, too, am to blame for thinking he could make you happy.'

'Nonsense! It was none of your doing. Even if we had met somewhere else, I know I would have fallen in love with him. Do you believe there is just one special man in the world, Pilar, that a woman will love, no matter what?'

'What is going on in that little mind, eh? Are you going with Senhor Sorrell or back to the *quinta*?'

'Neither. I am going to Sobral,' Natália declared. 'I know there is the possibility that he will refuse to see me, but I could stay with Alída . . .' Her lips quivered slightly as she considered the possibility of yet another rejection. 'I have to talk to him, and explain . . .'

'If you travel as the Senhora Natália Sorrell, the wife of a British officer and expect to be treated as such, I've no doubt he will hear of your coming long before you reach Sobral. If it is your intention to get to him without him receiving prior knowledge of your intentions, you

must do so by travelling as someone totally in-
conspicuous—such as a servant-girl. If you have the
courage, of course, *menina*?'

'Anyone has only to take one look at me to see I am no
servant,' Natália replied, stunned by the suggestion. She
had seen cart-loads of women on their way to the front
when she rode with Charles the previous day, laughing
and joking with the soldiers travelling with them. If she
did not travel under her own name, she might be taken
for one of them! Camp-followers—laundrywomen . . .
or one of the usual prostitutes who always trailed in the
wake of an army.

'It will be necessary to alter your appearance, to
darken your skin and cut off most of your hair. It would
be full of the most unmentionable things if it was left
long! Lord knows when you would be able to take a
proper bath!—and I may not always be able to stay close
at hand to watch over you, though I swear I shall try.
When I have finished with you, not even the Major
himself will know you,' Pilar added with a slow,
confident smile. 'Isn't that what you want?'

'Cut my hair? Darken my skin?' Natália looked at her
as if she had taken leave of her senses. She would not
have her name and rank to protect her . . . She would be
alone and unprotected until she reached Adam's side. It
was an idiotic plan . . . foolish . . . yet so daring that it
might just work. She could pretend she was on her way
to join Alída and her new husband! Yet why should she
place herself at risk for a man who did not care for her?
Who had twice denied her as his wife. She could not
imagine herself as a dusky-skinned servant-girl, and
balked at the thought of scissors being wielded on the
burnished gold hair of which she was so proud.

'Supposing, just supposing . . .' she began, then
broke off with a shake of her head as Pilar laid down the
brush. 'No! I cannot! And yet, if he did not know me . . .
I could stay with him . . . *make* him love me! He wanted

me that night, Pilar. I know he did! I gave him love, and he scorned me.'

'Do you seek him out to tell him you still love him and wish to be his wife—or do you want revenge, *menina*, to soothe your wounded pride? Perhaps you could make him fall in love with you? He is only a man, after all . . . And he will not know you.'

Now Pilar dared to raise the matter, Natália found herself pondering over her determination to follow her husband. She did love him, but he had hurt her. It would be no more than he deserved if she did not tell him who she was straight away.

'You want me to take a bath at this time of night?' Natália protested, only half awake and believing she had dreamed Pilar was waking her at two in the morning.

Pulling back the bedclothes, the maid pushed her feet into slippers and propelled her towards the adjoining room, where enormous closets lined the walls. On a large rush mat was a porcelain bath, delightfully decorated with pink rosebuds. Fresh towels were draped over a chair, together with a piece of a folded black cloth.

'It has been many years since I last mixed this particular concoction.' Pilar gave an odd smile as her mistress stared round her in bewilderment. 'I do not want the dye to stain the towels, or Senhor Sorrell might have me whipped for my part in this. He might, anyway.'

'He would not do such a thing; he is a kind man. Besides, you are my servant, I would not allow it . . .' Natália's eyes widened, flew to the bath and widened still more at the sight of the dark liquid there. 'Now? Pilar, you did not say it would be tonight!'

'It has to be done while everyone is asleep. You are afraid? That is understandable, but if you trust me you will take off your nightgown and soak yourself. An hour should be long enough. Some of the—ingredients— were very hard to come by, and two I could not get at all, so I had to add more walnut juice, which is why you must spend longer in it than usual. It felt quite like old times again.'

Natália looked at her sharply as she lowered herself into the bath. What did she mean? Pilar had been in her father's household for over twenty years, but no one, including herself, knew very much about the woman's background. The liquid terrified her. She would emerge coal-black, and never be able to get her skin clean again!

Sensing her reluctance, Pilar gave her no time for regrets. Taking up the pair of scissors which lay on top of the towels, she selected a thick wad of hair and began to cut. Natália gave a cry, and closed her eyes. What had she done!

'It is not as strong as it looks,' she was assured in a soothing tone. Snip—snip, the scissors continued their ruthless work as she talked. Natália sat bolt upright, her lips pressed tightly together, eyes firmly closed. 'In a moment, you must immerse yourself completely. If your eyebrows need more darkening, I can do that afterwards. You will make a very alluring waif, *menina*. Major Sorrell will stand no chance when he sees you. I'd forgotten how your hair used to curl when you were a little girl. When it is dry, it will do so again. Almost done . . . Be brave a little longer.'

Brave! She was shaking like an aspen-leaf by the time Pilar allowed her to emerge from the bath and wrapped the black cloth about her dripping body.

'Bring me a mirror quickly,' Natália insisted, but the maid shook her head.

'Not yet. Be patient and let me dry you. Then you are going back to bed. I shall bring you some hot milk, and you will sleep. Tomorrow we shall introduce the new maid to Dom Carlo. I took the liberty of spending some of the money on suitable clothes—nothing special, you understand, and stout walking sandals. Servants do not ride very often. Who knows what kind of conditions you will encounter once you reach the Linhas!'

'Let me see myself.' Grabbing up the trailing ends of the cloth about her, Natália brushed aside Pilar's restraining hand and ran back into the other room. Before the mirror, she came to an abrupt halt. She could feel the blood draining from her face at what confronted her, but it did not show. From beneath short, very black, wet hair, vivid blue eyes stared out of a strange face. Her skin glowed with a deep mahogany sheen. She did not look a freak! In fact the effect was quite becoming, and her heart skipped a beat to think that Adam might be drawn more to a dark-skinned serving-maid than he was to his own wife.

'He will not know you. Not when I have done.' Pilar began to dry her hair, watching her closely. 'You are pleased?'

'Yes, and unsure . . . and yet somehow confident. Pilar, you are wonderful! Where did you learn such things? What was in that awful mixture?'

'Herbs, and the dyes of certain plants.'

'As simple as that? I know the women in Alto Verde use the juice from wild irises to dye cloth, and I have heard that some of the young girls, when they wish to make themselves more attractive, darken their skin with oil from the olives. How they must smell!' Natália gingerly put her wrist beneath her nose. 'Thank goodness, I don't.'

'I must rinse your hair with lemon-juice and rose-water, and then, *menina*, you must sleep.'

'You haven't told me how you knew what to do. Are you a gipsy, Pilar? You've never admitted it—or denied it, either.'

'I am many things. But just this once, inquisitive one, I shall satisfy a little of your curiosity so that you may realise what can be achieved if you are prepared to be strong and fight for what you want. I was born into a poor family—the eighth girl. We were ten in all. By the time I was six, there were only three of us left. Starvation and sickness had claimed many of my brothers and sisters. My father deserted us when my mother could no longer bear children. She tried to support us all by helping the sick of the village. She had a way with herbs . . . a knowledge passed to her from her grandmother. She was repaid with fire. When she could not prevent the young son of the head-man of our village from dying, he ordered her to be burnt as a witch. I remember very little of the years after that. I ran away that day to prevent myself being sold into bondage. I lived as I could—stole what I had to—in order to stay alive. By chance, I came to Lisboa, and there found a home—for a while—with an old woman who plied a strange trade, as I was soon to discover. Many fine ladies and gentlemen came to her for her potions. Love-philtres—dyes for their hair when it began to grey—whiteners for their old skin. She knew it all. I sat and watched and listened. One day, she just died . . . and I began to roam again.'

'And you came to Alto Verde, near dead from hunger and fever,' Natália breathed. What a wealth of knowledge lurked behind that placid face. So many hardships, the loss of loved ones, yet she had survived.

'I was pretty once,' Pilar murmured, watching her with a hint of amusement in the depths of brown eyes. 'I learned quickly about the world—and men.'

Natália turned back to the mirror and surveyed herself in silence. Was she this lovely tantalising colour all over? Would it make her body more enticing to Adam? 'You have nothing to offer me. . . . You are a child playing at being a woman. I would rather pay for my pleasures than bed you.' His cruel, scathing remarks came back to her, heightening her resolve, hardening her senses against any traces of weakness. How was it possible that she wanted to hurt him? To inflict pain as he had done to her? She loved him!

* * *

Charles was having breakfast when Pilar came into the room followed by a dark-skinned girl dressed in a modest black skirt and dark blue blouse. She followed the maid with head downbent and hands clasped tightly together in front of her. Bare feet were thrust into leather sandals. A cross of silver hung on a chain about her neck.

'My mistress has bid me bring this girl to you, senhor. She found her begging in the street yesterday, near starving, and took pity on her. She intends to journey on to Sobral and thinks she might serve as a maid. But she wishes for your approval,' Pilar said coolly. 'I have bathed her—for she was filthy, of course. These beggar girls always are. But I fed her first, so she was fairly quiet while I scrubbed the grime from her skin. Do you find her presentable enough for my mistress, or shall I give her a coin and send her back into the streets where she belongs?'

'Oh, no, gracious senhor!' The girl gave a wail, and flung herself on the floor at Charles's feet, clutching at his trouser-leg and sobbing.

'Get up, girl, and let me look at you,' he demanded. He could scarcely suppress the gasp which rose to his lips as she straightened and he found himself staring into a pair of brilliant blue eyes, so like those of Natália that it momentarily stunned him.

'If your mistress wanted to take servants with her, she had only to inform me and I would have selected more suitable companions,' he declared, casting a dubious look at the quivering girl. Despite the colour of her eyes, which Natália was sure would give her away both to him and to Adam, she realised he did not know her.

'I have no family, senhor. My mother is dead and my father deserted us . . . May he burn in hell,' she muttered in a low, fierce whisper. 'I'll work. I swear it by the Holy Virgin! I can sew . . . and cook. Well, some,' she added, as Pilar's mouth twitched. She knew how to cook, for she had spent many hours in the kitchens watching the cook prepare bread and soups and learned how to mix the fiery piri-piri spices for special sauces —but as to the actual cooking, she had always had servants to do that for her.

So many times Pilar had taken pity on her and pretended she was indisposed, usually a malady of the stomach which would confine her to bed for at least two days—and always when her father was absent from the *quinta*. For one of those days, Natália would roam alone—and free—in the countryside, while Alída was being tutored. Then for blissful hours she would sit in a corner of the kitchen, listening to the gossip, envying the activity going on about her. Occasionally, when it was safe to do so, the cook would allow her to knead the dough and grind the spices. She revelled in flour up to her elbows, the smell of pimentos and onions, sweet-smelling garlic. There was much knowledge accumulated in her brain that had never been put to good use.

As Charles put aside his paper, she added with mischievous delight, 'Would you deny me the opportunity of cooking for my husband, senhor?'

His eyes flew to her face, scanning it intently. Recognition dawned. An oath broke from his lips . . . She steeled herself for anger . . . and heard him roar with laughter.

'Damn me if you might not bewitch him after all, looking like that! I take it that is your intention? Paying him back a little, maybe?'

'No,' Natália protested. 'Well, perhaps a little . . . But don't you agree I shall be able to get close to him like this? I shall pretend to be Alída's maid. I shall be near him . . . For now, that's all I ask.'

'I should forbid this, you know. I shall never forgive myself if anything happens to you. How do your propose to travel?'

'I—I hadn't thought . . .' She could not go by

carriage, as that was how ladies travelled. Servants walked . . .

'There is sure to be a supply wagon going to Sobral within the next few days. I shall see a friend of mine and you can travel with it. You are to let me know the moment you arrive in Sobral. Is that clear, my impulsive, marvellous *nora pequena*?'

He used the Portuguese word for 'daughter-in-law' with such warmth in his voice that Natália threw her arms about his neck and hugged him. She had grown very fond of Charles Sorrell.

'I shall be careful and send messages, I promise. Pilar will be with me. We shall be quite safe. I have to do this, don't you understand? I cannot bear to be without him. Even his scorn will be better than nothing at all!'

Charles looked into her determined features, and knew that nothing, short of taking her back with him to Lisboa by force, would prevent her from going to his son, and a silent pride swelled his heart to bursting-point.

'You are truly worthy of the Sorrell name.'

True to his word, before he returned to Lisboa, Charles made arrangements for two of his son's household to follow him to Sobral under the protection of a small supply wagon and ten soldiers. Natália had found herself crushed between sacks of flour, grain and coffee and sugar on one side, and the enormous bulk of one of the other four occupants, camp-followers on their way to look for the men who had left them behind in Mafra or Lisboa. Before the journey was a quarter of the way through, her cheeks were burning profusely from the coarseness of the banter passing between the women and the soldiers accompanying them. Now she realised what she was up against. She had been taken for one of them, although she insisted she was the maid of a lady of quality and on the way to rejoin her mistress.

Her remarks had been greeted with broad smiles and whispered comments. They thought her no better than they were!

She ignored their attempts to draw her into conversation, and averted her gaze from a young Lieutenant riding alongside the wagon who showed more than a passing interest in the slender, dusky young woman with eyes as blue as English cornflowers. She feigned sleep—wondering how it would be when she reached Sobral.

Pilar made the journey travelling in another wagon, which carried livestock. Pigs, and chickens to feed the hundreds of mouths waiting ahead. She said nothing when they were deposited in the dusty main street of the town after Natália had vigorously rejected a suggestion by the Lieutenant that he find her accommodation. She had a pretty shrewd idea where it would have been, and was glad to see the wagons roll on towards the warehouses which had been commandeered by the army on the edge of the town, but stood brushing feathers from her hair and clothes in obvious displeasure. Natália had supposed that Alída would have lodgings in the town, not close to the main front line, but all her questions as to the whereabouts of the Senhora Alída Sorrell, wife of Captain Drew Sorrell, came to nothing. Instead she received more than one most outrageous proposal which sent the blood rushing to her cheeks in embarrassment.

Often during the journey she had begun to wonder at the wiseness of her disguise. The blueness of her eyes was accentuated by the dark sheen of her skin. Her lips looked fuller, redder, than before. Black curls twisted about her ears, danced about her cheek. She looked different—felt different—and it was becoming obvious that men found her attractive. That was the strange part, even more difficult to accept than the stranger who faced her in the morning when she gazed into the mirror. She was no longer Natália Catarina Maria Lareira, tied by convention and the proud name she bore. No longer need she contain the untamed spirit her father had tried in vain to suppress. She was a simple servant-girl, and her heart was free to give to whom she pleased.

No, it was not free. It belonged to Adam, and always would. But now she could—and would—do something about it.

The closer they had come to Sobral, the more intense the devastation of the land, the heavier the fortifications. On the skyline, windmills and forts stood side by side. Earthworks like long black worms slithered across the bare earth. As they passed scattered villages, curious eyes watched them. Once they were ordered to stop by a patrol, but after the Lieutenant had spoken with the officer in charge, laughing as he gazed back at the wagon where the women sat, they were allowed through. Natália lifted a hand to push back a damp tendril of hair from her forehead. She hardly felt the discomfort of wet clothes, for they had been drenched in a brief shower an hour before, or the ache beginning to invade her legs and back from the bumpy ride. All she could think about was Adam!

They had arrived just as the watery sun was descending behind dark clouds for the last time that day. The air was heavy and oppressive, and distant thunder heralded the approach of a storm. Men sprawled or sat outside tiny *tascas* and wine shops, and betted whether it would come. Natália noticed more than one uniformed figure enjoying a game of dice, usually in the company of a woman.

'We must find Alída before it gets dark. Someone must know her,' Natália said, searching the street for someone to speak to again. Now she was not only tired, but beginning to realise how hungry she was as appetising smells came wafting through open windows.

'Well, now, decided to wait for me after all, have

you?' The young Lieutenant was standing behind them, eyeing her with the same candour as he had when she had sat in the wagon.

'I am still looking for my mistress. She is the wife of Captain Drew Sorrell, of the Light Dragoons. Please tell me if you know where they are? I was to have arrived yesterday, and she will be angry with me.'

'Sorrell? Both Captain Sorrell and his brother are on the other side of Monte Agraço, girl. Not here.'

'Not—not here?'

'You stupid girl!' Pilar pushed her to one side and faced the officer, her dark eyes flashing with anger. 'I told her the mistress was not in the town, but this idiot would insist we tried here first. I'll take a stick to her if we don't find the Captain before the rain starts. My bones won't stand a soaking again . . . And that ride . . . Senhor, you have a kind face . . . For pity's sake, will you tell us where to find the Captain?'

'Better than that, I'll take you to them. Captain Sorrell is my commanding officer. I have dispatches for him from Mafra, so you are welcome to travel with me if you wish. But as for getting there before the rain comes . . .' He looked down at the raindrops already soaking into his blue sleeve. 'You'll have to share a mule, but I should be able to find you some protective clothing. It's the best I can do, and you must keep up with me. I'm not too delighted to get another soaking either, and I want to reach camp as quickly as possible.'

'*Obrigada, senhor*. I shall remember you in my prayers,' Pilar murmured, and Natália managed to add a few words of gratitude herself, so overcome with relief at the news that she felt quite faint.

'I am sure my kindness will not go unappreciated.' The Lieutenant was looking at Natália as he spoke, and, to her horror, as he passed her, he soundly pinched her bottom!

*   *   *

It took more than an hour from Sobral along winding tracks, that were more like rivers of mud now as the heavens opened and a deluge of rain descended upon the Lieutenant and his two women companions and the escort of five troopers riding behind them. A fierce wind buffeted the riders mercilessly, forcing Natália to grip tightly to the pommel of the saddle. Pilar, her arms tight around her mistress's waist, muttered prayer after prayer for their safe arrival, and reproached herself for bringing her 'baby' on such a dangerous and obviously godforsaken journey. If He had wanted her to be reunited with Adam Sorrell, he would have been at the house in Mafra . . . They would not have had to make another journey, on a stubborn mule who would not go at more than a snail's pace, despite the driving rain. Natália would not have had to suffer the indignities of being ogled by the soldiers.

Both women were reeling with tiredness and discomfort when a long low building came into sight a few yards ahead. So blinding was the rain that they were upon it before it was possible to define whether it was in fact a place of habitation, or a deserted peasant hut now only used by brave shepherds and goat-herders when watching their flocks.

Natália almost fell out of the saddle into the waiting arms of the young officer, but the moment her feet touched the ground, she quickly pulled away. She wanted to give him no encouragement—not that he needed any, for with a wicked grin, he grabbed her up in his arms and ran with her into the shelter of the house, leaving poor Pilar to be helped down by one of the troopers, who only at the last moment realised she was still sitting on the *burro* and turned back to lift her from it.

The house was one of many which had been commandeered by the army when its occupants retreated behind the safety of the lines. The long, oak-beamed kitchen with its enormous open fire and the smell of baking coming from the oven, set back in four feet of solid wall, was a welcome sight to Natália, who sank immediately into the nearest chair.

Her wet clothes clung to her uncomfortably, and the way her companion was eyeing the shapely figure outlined beneath them did nothing to ease her discomfort. Through a low doorway appeared a man, and she quickly lowered her head as Drew advanced towards the table where the Lieutenant had laid down his dispatch-pouch while he shook the water from his cape and shako, and straightened the very sad-looking red plume.

'You've made good time, Lieutenant. Didn't beat the rain, though. I was hoping it would hold off until tomorrow,' he said cheerfully, oblivious of the water soaking the stone floor. 'Have you eaten yet? My wife has some good vegetable soup on the stove. You are welcome to stay and have some.'

'I am afraid I always put too much garlic in my soups for the Lieutenant. He prefers Nuno's chicken with vegetables.' Alída came into the room, and Natália blinked in surprise at her appearance. Her hair was pulled back into a tight knot at the nape of her neck. She was wiping her hands on an apron tied about her waist. Her dress was plain blue cotton, and on her feet were leather sandals. Natália had harboured deep reservations about her sister being able to cope with the hardships and deprivations endured by soldiers' wives, but now they vanished. Her smile was quite dazzling, even though there were grey shadows beneath her eyes as if she lacked a good night's sleep.

Natália's stomach had growled when soup was mentioned, but now to consider a plate of chicken and vegetables, it positively ached. The Lieutenant took the hand extended to him and touched still damp fingers to his lips. He obviously had the utmost respect for the Captain's wife, and treated her with the courtesy he would have shown if she had been greeting him in some elegant drawing-room in the capital.

'With no offence to your cooking, ma'am, I've been drowned twice today and I'd like to get into dry clothes. After that, some warming brandy and, as you say, Nuno's chicken. Where that boy gets them from I'll never know, but while he has them, I'll eat them! I was brought up on a farm, and my appetite demands four large meals a day.' Then, remembering the two silent women who stood behind him, 'I've brought you the servants you were expecting. They came up from Mafra with me. Good night, Captain Sorrell. Mrs Sorrell.'

At the word 'servants', Alída's gaze flew to the two faces. One she did not recognise, but the other . . .

'Pilar! Oh, my dear woman, you are drowned . . . What are you doing here?' She flew to her side, pulling away the blanket in which she was enveloped and dropping it on the floor. 'Come to the fire and warm yourself. Drew, fetch some soup for them both. Nothing is wrong? Natália . . . Father?'

'*Nada, senhora, nada,*' Pilar assured her, as she pulled off wet shoes and rolled down her stockings under Drew's amused eyes.

'You've come to play bodyguard, have you then? She is quite safe with me, you know! We are in no danger here.'

They took no notice of Natália until that moment when she, too, drew close to the fire and divested herself of the coat one of the troopers had wrapped round her when the rain began. Pilar was the only person they were interested in because they recognised her . . . Hope rose inside her. If she could fool them . . . !

'May I stay by the fire, senhora, and have a little soup?' she asked in a meek tone, and Drew quickly fetched another earthenware bowl and filled it with piping hot soup crammed full of vegetables.

'I don't know you . . .' Alída turned to give her her

full attention. 'Pilar, I have no need of a maid up here
. . . I have little enough to do, as it is.' She broke off, her
eyes narrowing in disbelief as the bedraggled newcomer
reached for the bowl, and she found herself staring at
long, slender fingers with nails manicured, not broken or
dirty as she would have expected. It could not be!
'Perhaps I do . . .'

Lifting her head, Natália stared first at her sister and
then into Drew's astonished face, and heard his sharp
intake of breath as recognition dawned and she said
stubbornly,

'I am not going back. I have come to find Adam and
stay with him. I know what you said in your letter. He
doesn't want me, but I love him and I shall make him
accept me'.

'The moment he sees you, he'll send you back to
Mafra and not be polite about it,' Drew said harshly.
'Are you mad, Natália? Whatever possessed you to
arrive here looking like—like that? Good heavens, girl,
you might have been taken for . . .'

He broke off as Alída flashed him a warning glance,
but Natália smiled and only shrugged her wet shoulders.

'A camp-follower? You would not believe the pro-
posals I have received already! More than one from the
Lieutenant who brought us here, I might add. If that is
what I have to become to be with Adam, so be it.'

'She has taken leave of her senses! Thank God the rain
has delayed him, or he would have been here when she
arrived.' Drew ran a hand exasperatedly through his
unruly hair. 'She can return to Mafra in the morning. I'll
arrange it.'

'No,' Alída stated firmly, and he looked at her as if he
had not heard aright. 'She will stay here. Are you so
blind, my husband? She loves Adam as deeply as I love
you. I am here with you. Would you deny her the right to
be with her husband?'

'You know how he feels about her?'

'I know his pride has been hurt and that she is the only one he can take it out on,' Alída retorted. 'Let Natália have her way. If she fails, she must return to Mafra or to the *quinta* and accept that the marriage will be annulled. But, if she succeeds . . .'

'Are you telling me she intends to crawl into Adam's bed pretending to be a camp-woman?' Drew snorted, unable to believe such a conversation was going on. 'You have seen the kind of women about here . . . some are wives, true, but the rest are little more than paid whores who will find another man if the one they are with goes into battle and gets killed!'

'There is a difference,' Natália told him quietly, and something in her tone halted his mounting anger. There was not only determination on the dark face, but pride too. 'Until such time as the marriage is annulled . . .'

'Father is arranging that.'

'Not yet.' She smiled again, a knowing, confident smile that told him she had won the heart of Charles Sorrell and gained precious time to put her audacious scheme into effect. 'Until the marriage is annulled, I am still his wife. He is my husband. There is nothing wrong in what I do. Now, I am very hungry, and poor Pilar is near dead with cold. Have you somewhere we can dry our clothes and rest?'

For a long moment there was silence, and Alída began to look quite anxious as her husband did not speak. Then, with a lifting of his shoulders which indicated defeat, Drew said,

'Take them away. They are your responsibility. I'll try and find some more bedding and clothes. God help us all when Adam gets back!'

CHAPTER EIGHT

THE SMALL detachment of cavalry under Drew's command had made itself comfortable around the farmhouse. Some soldiers, preferring the luxury of a roof over their heads instead of the draughty bivouacs spread along the river bank, had taken over an enormous barn and slept beside their horses and an assortment of other animals. Encamped at the far end, well away from the family men and their wives, were the women who had drifted in from the towns and villages. Between the heavily protected fort at Sobral and the cavalry was situated a battery of cannon which was trained on the distant countryside, guarded by a large contingent of infantry.

Natália spent the first few days after her arrival playing 'maid' to her sister whenever she went out. Even in the house, Pilar often insisted she maintained the pose just in case any strangers appeared unexpectedly. It was not as easy as Natália had thought it would be.

She did not precede Alída through the door, Pilar reproved, but walked a respectful distance to the rear. Neither did she speak unless she was spoken to. If there were guests, she did not linger in the room, expecting to be able to listen to the conversation. Natália did not argue, even though she found it most difficult to contain her questions whenever she saw Drew speaking with one of his men. Surely someone knew where Adam was, and when he would return? He was overdue, and although Drew shrugged off the possibility that he might have been captured by the enemy, she knew it was in his mind.

When he returned, Adam would sleep in the room

adjoining that which Natália shared with Pilar. On several occasions she had been tempted to go into it, but the presence of Nuno always deterred her. He guarded the door from within during the day, Alída told her, and spent his time brushing Adam's uniform, polishing his boots, and accumulating vintage brandy for his return. At night he slept outside the door, his body stretched across the opening, making it impossible for anyone to enter without waking him. Alída thought him a very useful acquisition to her scanty household, for if there was ever anything she wanted in the way of food or wines, she had only to tell the boy and they would appear within a few hours.

He had stared quite rudely at Natália the first time they encountered each other, but after that he had ignored her. He had scarcely seen her for more than a few minutes at a time, Natália knew, and so there was no possibility of his associating the drably-dressed serving-maid with the younger daughter of Senhor Abílio Lareira.

Determined to carry out every duty required of her, however distasteful, Natália accompanied Pilar each day to the river, and for the first time in her life found herself washing dirty clothes, pounding them against flat stones until they were clean, and then spreading them over near-by bushes to dry in the hot autumn sunshine. Here, to her relief, she found she was accepted without reservations. If anyone gave her a second glance, it was to envy the sooty lashes veiling large blue eyes or the mop of short curls as black as a raven's wing. Another servant-girl—pretty enough, perhaps, to catch the eye of a British officer—but no one important.

Natália had forced herself to accept that, in her disguise, she seemed to be more attractive to men and must be careful not to give any of the women cause for jealousy and so bring unnecessary trouble down upon her head. It was impossible to stop the soldiers speaking to her, for many of them whiled away bored hours on the river bank, watching the women as they worked. Many tried to make assignations with her, and she found the easiest way to deter them was to pretend not only did she not understand one word of English, but that she was also a little simple-minded.

The only person on whom this did not have the desired effect was the Lieutenant who had brought her to Sobral. Much to Alída's amusement, Pilar's consternation and Natália's frustration, the young man persisted in his efforts to strike up a friendship. Or, as the latter suspected, a more binding liaison.

On some pretext he would appear at the farmhouse, usually as they were all about to eat an evening meal. With no one but Drew and Alída about, Natália and Pilar would sit at the table, but with the presence of a stranger, Natália was forced to help Pilar to serve the food and then conduct herself as a mere servant until he had departed.

It was a great relief when he did not appear for several days and she was allowed to enjoy her simple meals in peace. One evening, however, when she went down to the river to fetch water, he was waiting for her. The brief but fierce tussle that ensued when he grabbed hold of her and soundly kissed her, ended when the stone flagon she had just filled was emptied over his head, completely soaking him from head to toe.

Consumed with blind panic as he called her a very unladylike name and tried to grab her again, Natália picked up her skirts and ran—only to collide headlong with a bearded, ill-dressed man leading a limping horse through the trees.

'Oh—look where are you going!' she cried angrily, oblivious of the hand that caught and steadied her as she thudded into him. Her nose wrinkled at the odour clinging to him—sweat—the smell of horses—tobacco. She looked up in disgust at the grime-covered brown features—and froze in disbelief and horror.

A strangled cry escaped her lips as she took to her heels again, leaving Adam staring after her, too shocked by the image which had momentarily presented itself to him to move for several minutes. Those eyes! Her eyes! But the face of a gipsy wench! Was the memory of his accursed wife never to leave him? She haunted his dreams at night . . . Was he now to see her in every woman he met?

He was tired, he reasoned. A good bottle of brandy inside him, and then twelve hours' straight sleep, and he would be rational again. How could he ever have compared that creature with Natália? Her skin was as white and smooth as alabaster. Her lips softly coloured. Her body . . . He swore under his breath and continued on his way again, shutting out the memory of his wedding night. The brief but hard contact of the girl's body against his had made him remember how much he had wanted to possess the wife he did not even acknowledge and longed to be rid of. By now his father would be arranging the annulment. When he returned to Lisboa, the unpleasant episode would be over and he would be free. How strange that the knowledge did not give him the satisfaction it had done a few weeks ago!

Alída was sitting on the velvet-covered couch someone had requisitioned from Sobral and brought to the farmhouse to give them a little comfort. It was very out-of-place amid the pine table and the hard chairs, but for a little while each evening it gave her a memory of home as she sat close to Drew and they talked in low tones, their heads close together. They did not mean to shut her out, Natália realised, but the sight of them holding hands, kissing, listening to the warmth and affection in their voices, made her feel dismally unhappy.

Her sister looked up startled as she burst through the door, and Drew came to his feet with a stifled exclamation as he saw her distraught features.

'Natália! What . . . ?'

'He's back!' Natália could scarcely speak. 'Adam . . .
Back by the river . . .'

Without pausing in her headlong flight, she carried on
into her room and slammed the door behind her, to sink
quivering on the bed. Back—safe—as she had prayed
he would be! Could he have recognised her? Trembling
still in every limb, she rose and went to look at herself in
the piece of glass she had propped on the rickety table.
No. Pilar's potions had worked strong magic. The face
which stared back at her bore no resemblance whatsoever to that of Natália Catarina Maria Lareira. So long
as she did not lose her head and betray herself, she was
safe!

He had looked so exhausted. Where had he been,
what horrors had he seen, to make him look so drained,
as if the weight of the whole world was bearing upon his
shoulders? Loud voices came from the other side of the
door. Drew's, harsh with the relief at seeing his brother
again. Alída's, high-pitched with the strain she too had
felt, urging him to sit down and rest, to have food and
drink. Nuno's trying to make itself heard in the babble of
conversation. He would prepare a bath at once for the
Major, and bring a bottle of his best brandy while he
lazed in the hot water. Natália stood beside the door, yet
dared not venture out. Her welcome must be said in
silence, her tears unseen. The shock of seeing him made
her feel quite faint, and she was so long in gathering her
composure that Pilar came to fetch her.

'You must come, there is work to be done,' she hissed.
'There is some left-over meat we can mix with rice and
vegetables for the Major. He has not eaten in two days.
The boy is heating some bath-water for him. I thought he
would fall asleep the moment he sat down . . . The poor
man is exhausted, but now he and his brother are deep
into soldier talk. Quickly, *menina*. Is this not what you
have been waiting for?'

It was, Natália reasoned, and with a deep breath, nodded assent. Why should he recognise her if others had not? And if he did, he could only send her away. Before he did that, she would say what she had come to say. Either way, she had nothing to lose . . . perhaps a husband to win back!

She hurried past Adam, sprawled in a chair, his long booted legs stretched out before him, and began to help Pilar to prepare some food. Nuno had already brought a bottle of brandy and poured a large glass for his master. Drew was too much interested in what his brother was saying to touch the one on the table in front of him. Natália positioned herself to one side of the fire so that she could watch them—or rather Adam. He had discarded his jacket. The shirt beneath was as grubby as the rest of his clothes, she saw. There was no sign of the elegant officer she had been introduced to at Alto Verde, or the handsome, casually clad man who had ridden with her the next day.

This man was a stranger. The tired brown face was considerably harder than she remembered it, and there was anger in the taut jawline as he spoke of the French atrocities he had seen, perpetrated by Masséna's scouts as they scoured the country for informers, for food and women. Men hid their wives and daughters when they approached—sometimes successfully, but not always, for as the French rampaged through village after village searching for non-existent stores of food, the unfortunate women were often discovered and abused. Examples were made of anyone showing resistance. Age was of no consequence, Adam told the hushed listeners. He had himself cut down the body of a six-year-old boy who had been hanged, together with his father and two brothers.

'There were times when I envisaged you coming to such a ghastly end,' Drew intervened at one point, and reached for his glass for the first time.

'You know I bear a charmed life. I would have been back to rendezvous with you on time had we not run into a French courier. A very obliging fellow, as it happened. After Julío had talked with him for a while, he handed over all his dispatches quite willingly and told us a great deal we didn't know before. For one, that Robert Carrington had got himself captured and was on his way to Masséna himself. If they had broken him . . .'

'Who . . . ?' Alída began, but Drew had anticipated her question.

'A fellow officer—in the same line of work as Adam. Well, go on, man. Where is he? Did you get to him? You did go after him? That's why you are late, isn't it?'

'By now he's with the surgeon in Sobral. He was in quite a state when I managed to lift him from under the French noses, but he survived the ride back and I've every hope he will mend within a few weeks. They gave us a beating, though. I had only ten men against forty. Now I have six. Four good men . . . I won't forget that . . .'

Adam drained his glass and refilled it and drank again, then laid his head against the back of the chair with a heavy sigh.

'Alída, I'm sure your cooking is as excellent as when I went away, but I don't have the stomach for it just now.'

'A meal would do you far more good than the brandy you are drinking,' Alída reproved. 'Won't you try a little?'

Natália quickly ladled a large amount of rice and meat on to a platter and placed it before him. For the first time since entering, Adam became aware of not only her presence, but that of Pilar also. He stared long and hard at both women, his brows drawn together into a suspicious frown.

Alída said, 'I am a lady of leisure again, even in the midst of a war. My father sent Pilar to be with me.'

'And her?' Adam's eyes seemed to bore into Natália's

soul. Somehow she feigned ignorance of his scrutiny and placed the pot of coffee over the fire to reheat.

'A girl I found in Sobral last week,' Alída said calmly, while Drew floundered for words. He knew he should stop this, but he could not. 'She has Natália's eyes, hasn't she? I think that's what first attracted her to me. She was begging in the streets, poor thing. Now that Pilar has cleaned her up, she is quite presentable. A little simple, but willing enough to work, and conditions here are rather primitive for someone like myself who has been cosseted all her life.'

She bestowed a dazzling smile on Adam, who gradually relaxed in his seat and turned his attention to the food before him. But he only picked at it, and pushed it away after the second mouthful.

'Forgive me, I've no stomach for it. Tomorrow I promise I shall eat like a horse. Nuno, is my bath hot?' He rose to his feet, stretching cramped limbs. His eyes flickered towards Natália as he turned towards his room.

'*Sim, chefe*, and I have a fresh bottle for you.'

'I shall be asleep before I can drink it, but the thought is appreciated.' Adam gripped his shoulder for a brief moment as he passed the boy, and Nuno's face glowed with pride. Natália crushed the pain which rose in her. Smiles and kind words for his brother and Alída, even for Nuno, but nothing for the wife who must remain a stranger to him.

He followed the boy into his room. A few minutes later, Nuno reappeared with an armful of clothes.

'The Major wishes these to be washed.' He dropped them at Natália's feet. 'There is no hurry. He will not require them for a while.'

'I'll do them in the morning,' Pilar said, and bent to gather them up again. She had caught sight of the rebellious gleam in Natália's eyes, and knew she had to act quickly to prevent the girl from inadvertently giving herself away at the lad's cheekiness. Bundling them into a cupboard, she snatched up a clean towel and a large piece of soap and thrust them out towards the silent girl.

'It's time you did some work round here, my girl! The mistress is too easy with you. Take these, and go and attend the Major.'

'That's my job . . .' Nuno began to protest, but Pilar waved a hand towards the door. Alída and Drew exchanged amused glances at the capable way the woman had taken charge. Poor Natália, expected to scrub her husband's back like a serving-girl! Still, she wanted to get close to him.

'It's woman's work. You have better things to do. What about the Major's horse? Has it been fed and watered? Have you laid out clean clothes for the morning? Is his bed aired? *Meu Deus*, boy, you have more than enough to do! Let this lazy creature work for the food she eats. Well, girl, are you going to stand there all night?'

Natália could feel the colour creeping into her cheeks as she left the room. Adam was her husband, and so there was no shame in waiting on him while he took a bath . . . but she had never seen him unclothed! The room was very quiet as she gingerly pushed open the door. He was immersed in the tub of hot water, a familiar long, black *cigarrillo* between his lips. On the floor within easy reach was a bottle of brandy, and the silver goblet she had often seen Nuno polishing with loving care. He looked asleep.

She half turned, grateful of the chance to extricate herself from this very precarious position, when, without opening his eyes, he muttered, 'What do you want? Where's Nuno?'

'He—he has gone to see your horse, senhor. I—I was told to bring you these.' She held out the towel and soap, and one eye eased open to regard her standing apprehensively on the threshold.

'Come in and close the door. You can scrub my back

now that you are here. It feels as if it has a week's grime still embedded in it.'

'*Sim, senhor.*' Somehow Natália forced herself to the side of the tub, conscious of Adam staring at her with narrowed gaze. Quickly she moved behind him, and lathering the soap, began to rub it into the smooth dark shoulders. Instantly memories came flooding back. How she had lain in his arms the night of the wedding and had felt the same strong muscles flexing beneath her fingers as he kissed her. The strength of his embrace—the dominating will that had taken her by storm.

Suddenly her nervousness vanished, and it became the most natural thing in the world to lather his arms and neck, the thick black hair and the firm chest with its dark curls. Unknowingly, the lightness of her touch became almost a caress, and Adam found himself relaxing more and more beneath the long tapered fingers which soothed the aches from his body as if by some miracle.

'Your fingers have magic in them, *moça*,' he said softly.

'Oh! You have a grey hair!' Natália could have bitten off her tongue at the thoughtless remark, but so great was her surprise—for she knew she had not noticed the silver thread at Alto Verde—that the words were uttered before she could contain them.

Adam's eyes searched her face, and then he gave a low, amused laugh. 'I'm no youngster any more. Only one? I'm lucky.'

'The senhor is a very brave man to do what he does,' Natália murmured, quickly changing the conversation to hide her confusion. He began to rise from the tub. With a gasp, she snatched up the towel and thrust it into his hands before deliberately dropping the soap and turning away to look for it. Behind her, more laughter, and Adam's voice mocking gently.

'You can turn round. I'm quite decent!'

He stood dripping wet on the bare floor, the towel

wrapped about his waist, water still glistening in the black hair, and a wicked smile on his face as he replenished the silver goblet with brandy. For a long moment he stared down into those large blue eyes and felt once more as if he were drowning.

'Go and see that my horse has been well cared for. Tell Nuno he need not come back here tonight. I am sure he has some pretty wench he's wanting to meet. You, perhaps?' The intensity of his thoughts made his tone harsh.

'No, senhor. I do not have a *noivo*,' Natália replied quietly. 'Does the senhor require me to return with news of his horse—or just to return?'

'And whose idea would that be? Not yours, I'll warrant! My brother's? Or his wife's? What I want is peace and quiet, *moça*. Sleep. I can take my pick of a dozen women if the fancy takes me, so why should I choose someone from the back alleys of Sobral?' He was deliberately cruel because he wanted her to stay. The realisation shocked him!

'The way the senhor has been staring at me, I thought perhaps I reminded him of someone he cared for.'

'The woman in my thoughts has eyes as blue as yours, girl, but I feel no affection for her.'

He thought of her! No matter what he said to Drew, or tried to pretend to himself, she was in his thoughts, Natália realised. She had to be bold. Play the hussy if necessary. So long as he did not send her away . . .

'Then perhaps I can make you forget her,' she said softly, and a derisive gleam came into the green depths of the eyes which swept her from head to toe.

'Perhaps you can. Come back if you wish.' With a shrug, Adam turned away and began to dry himself. Was he out of his mind? He did not really want the girl—not in that way! Since leaving Alto Verde he had not even looked at another woman, despite many invitations from ladies in the town. He did not socialise at all except with his men. He had even drawn apart from Drew since his marriage. He could not expect his brother to become involved with his problems or try to deal with his black moods when he had a young, pretty wife demanding all his attention.

It was strange that Pilar had been sent to care for Alída. Had she quarrelled with Natália or had Dom Abílio sent her to spy on him, perhaps to try to get him to return and accept his wife? Never! He was done with her! It was the waiting that tried his nerves, he told himself. Once he was free again, he would be able to sleep soundly at night. She would become nothing more than a bad dream that disappeared with the coming of morning. A reassuring thought—why, then, was every muscle in his body tense, his senses alert, listening for the footstep which would herald the return of the servant-girl with Natália's eyes?

When she returned, he would send her away. It was the only decent thing to do. If he took her to his bed, he would vent all his anger and bitterness on an innocent girl merely because she had the unfortunate mischance to possess eyes of the same colour as his wretched wife. He was not that kind of man! No, he would give her a coin.

He watched her slip silently through the door and close it behind her. The window behind him was open, and a light breeze invaded the room, bringing with it the rich perfume of orange-blossom. The muted glow from the single candle on the table beside the bed enhanced the colour of the girl's skin, giving it a rich copper glow. He could see the rise and fall of her breasts beneath the ill-fitting dress, as though she had been running and was out of breath. In haste to return to him? The little fool did not realise how she would be used! She was probably desperate for money, and anxious to please him with her willingness. Another reason not to take advantage of her. He felt himself begin to waver, remembering how

pleasant it had been to feel the softness of her against
him even for one brief moment. Quickly turning away,
he picked up the coin he had placed on the table and held
it out to her.

'Take this and go. You have done enough for me.'

Natália could not believe her ears. He was sending her
away! What had changed his mind? She did not move.
She might not get such a chance again. She would not
give up so easily.

'Did you not hear me, girl?' Damn her, Adam
thought, why did she look at him as if he had struck her?
He was offering her money, not a beating. 'Come, now,
don't tell me I offend you?' He gestured with the coin
again. 'Take it. Buy yourself a pretty dress.'

Still no reply. No movement. He uttered a curse as he
stepped forward and saw tears glistening in her eyes.
And more. A reproach so terrible that it seared his soul.
He was being condemned for being noble. Heaven
above! Without a word, she turned to the door. As her
hand reached for the latch, Adam said quietly, 'Stay.'

When Natália awoke the following morning, she was
alone. Only the imprint on the pillow beside her told her
it had not been a dream. She had shared her husband's
bed, but she was still not his wife! And then, directly in
her line of vision as she lay listening to singing in the
kitchen, a sound so reminiscent of the *quinta*, she saw
the coin he had offered her the night before. There was
nothing else on the table except that, and she came up in
the bed as if stung by a vicious insect. Its meaning was
only too clear. Payment for her services. How dare he!
She had stayed because she wanted to. She had made
that quite clear. She did not want him to think she did
this kind of this every night, with any man who took her
fancy. It may be the custom among other women in the
camp, she had told him, but it was not hers. And now he
had had the effrontery to shame her with payment! How

often had he done this before with others?

Her lips compressing into a tight, angry line, she leaned over and took the coin and threw it against the far wall. Pilar gave her a scrutinising look when she emerged to join them again, but the set features deterred her from venturing a question. Even Alída waited until breakfast was over before taxing her sister with what had taken place. Her only reply was a shrug of slim shoulders and the single word *'Nada.'* Nothing. Before she could recover from her astonishment, Natália had snatched Adam's clothes from the cupboard and hurried out of the house.

'I don't believe it,' Alída breathed, turning to her husband. 'Did Adam say anything to you?'

'Why should he? He is his own master. I told you the crazy scheme would not work. He hasn't looked at another woman since he walked out on Natália. Nor will he. It is too painful for him.'

'All the more reason to seek solace with someone sympathetic, then, who is willing to listen to his troubles. Servant-girls are always good listeners.'

'You don't know my brother,' Drew returned with a half-smile. 'Whatever happened between them—if anything—is their business, not ours, and if you care at all for your sister, you will send her home before she is hurt. Last night Adam was damned tired—too tired to recognise her, but if she stays, he might be tempted to take a second look. Maybe a third. It's what you are both hoping for, I know . . . But consider the consequences, I beg you.'

'I already have, and so has Natália. The decision to go or stay is hers alone. I won't make her leave,' Alída replied firmly. 'Pilar, go after her. See if you can make her tell you what took place.'

'That would not be wise, senhora.' The woman turned from the window, a deep smile curving around her full mouth. 'The Major is with her.'

'Answer me, girl!' Adam thundered. Curious faces turned in their direction, and he scowled and lowered his voice so that it did not carry beyond the two of them. The river bank was lined with women washing clothes, who had stared at him and passed comments as he strode towards the spot where Natália was engrossed in trying to get his shirt clean. 'Why did you not take the coin I left for you?'

When he had found it in a corner of the room, he had known instantly what had happened and had been seized with an unexplicable anger towards her. She had nothing. She was nothing, yet she refused his money! Proud little fool! There were not many like her about.

'Was it not enough?' he taunted, tight-lipped.

Slowly Natália raised her head and looked up at him. A thin sheen of perspiration shone upon her skin from her exertions. She wore no hat to protect her head, even though the sun was beating down on her mercilessly, for Pilar had told her that exposure to its rays would prolong her colouring and make it less vulnerable to fading. His eyes were drawn to the front of her dress, which was wet where she had splashed water from the river down the front of it as she leaned over too far and almost lost her balance. She sat back on her heels, holding his gaze, though it took all her will-power to do so. A damp tendril of hair lay across one cheek. His fingers itched to brush it away, and he was glad when she did so. The same reproach was in her gaze, and he did not understand why. What had he done wrong?

'I asked for no payment. I stayed with you because I wanted to.'

'Then you are angry because I fell asleep.' He had been holding her in his arms, feeling content and relaxed. She had been stroking his hair, her lips against his cheek . . . when, without warning, sleep had claimed him. And the brandy, he mused, remembering how he had awakened, and for some while seeing her lying beside him, had not been able to remember what it had been like making love to her. 'I apologise if I have injured your pride, *moça*, but if it's any consolation, I haven't slept so well for months. Not a single dream.'

Until he said it, he had not realised how peaceful his repose had been. No nightmares, no dreams of Natália taunting him from their wedding bed. How many nights had he relived that night?

'I am glad I was of some small use,' Natália returned coldly, returning her attention to the shirt at her feet.

'That in itself is worth something,' Adam replied, reaching for the coin he had brought with him. Something in him was determined she should have it. His consience, perhaps?

'No.' Her voice cut across him like a whiplash. A woman nearby laughed, and whispered to her companions, who looked at them. One pulled the neck of her blouse lower over her shoulders, invitingly. She obviously thought Natália had just turned down the English officer who was making his availability plain. 'There is much anger in you, senhor. Much pain. I thought I could make you forget whatever it is that troubles you for a few hours at least. I was wrong, but that is no reason for you to treat me like a woman of the streets. Please leave me alone. I have work to do.'

When she looked up, Adam was striding towards his horse among the trees. He rode away without turning back. He was not at the house when she returned with his clothes clean and dry, and she gave them to Nuno to put away. She shut herself in her room for most of the afternoon, refusing to answer any questions. Nothing had happened, she told both Alída and Pilar in an adamant tone, and nothing would now. Adam did not find her attractive, and she had refused the one chance of getting close to him again. She should have taken the money, she told herself. She was, after all, only a servant-girl. A penniless nobody. She had too much pride! He had wounded that pride, and she had struck back. It had been the wrong thing to do. Now he was lost to her for ever.

'Do you like my master?' Nuno stared at her across the flames of the fire. He was roasting a scrawny chicken on a spit over the red-hot ashes of some almond branches. She had left the house to escape her sister's searching looks and Pilar constantly hovering at her side, nudging her from time to time as if to prompt her into explanations, and sought solace beside the solitary figure.

Natália lifted her shoulders in a noncommittal shrug. 'I do not know him.'

'You stayed with him last night. He has not had a woman for a long time. Not since . . ' The boy stopped, and jabbed the chicken viciously with his knife.

'Since when . . .' Since Alto Verde? Was she the last woman he had really looked at and wanted to make love to? She did not want to believe he was in the habit of inviting servant-girls or women of easy virtue to his bed. But was he not only a soldier, but a lonely man—a bitter man? All women would be the same to him!

'I don't remember.' Nuno speared the food on to an earthenware platter, stared at her for a moment, then tore it in two and motioned her to help herself. Natália could barely conceal her delight. He was a most uncommunicative young man where anyone other than Adam was concerned. To be offered part of his evening meal was an acceptance she had not expected.

'You will go back tonight?' he asked at length.

'No. He does not want me. But I would like to be his woman. To belong to him. I have no one.'

'Then you are a fool,' Nuno said sharply. 'He belongs to no one, not even his wife. She, least of all, has a claim on him.' He broke off with an angry frown. 'It is not right for me to talk of things which are none of my business —or yours. Eat your chicken before than old dragon comes looking for you.'

'She is asleep.' Natália could not help smiling at the reference to Pilar. She bit into the leg she had taken from the platter, and some of the spicy sauce the boy had basted it with ran down from her mouth to her chin. She wiped it away with the back of her hand, imagining her father's face to see her eating like a common peasant. It was delicious. She licked her greasy fingers and reached for more.

A small furry shape materialised from the shadows beyond the fire and came rubbing round her bare legs. It was a small, very skinny cat. Its mottled coat of red and brown, streaked with fawn markings, was matted and dirty. It mewed pitifully, and she dropped a piece of chicken-skin at its feet. It pounced on the morsel as if ravenous, and Nuno gave a derisive laugh.

'You are soft! I knew it. I have chased that wretched thing away for the past two days. It should learn to fend for itself. If you spoil it, it will come back again and again. As you will return to the Major, whether he sends you away or not.'

'Everyone should have someone,' Natália replied quietly. The kitten at her feet mewed again and rubbed its scrawny little back along her legs. With a soft laugh, she picked it up and fed it more tiny pieces of chicken. 'Even a dejected creature like this needs someone. Now it has me.'

'Can you not do better than a flea-ridden stray cat?' a voice remarked from behind her, and Adam stepped into the firelight. Immediately, Nuno jumped to his feet and took the reins of his horse.

'Are you hungry, *chefe*? I have a cold chicken and wine.'

'Keep it for breakfast. I have eaten well—with Lord Wellington himself, as a matter of fact. I have been recommended for a promotion. What do you say to that, my young friend?'

Natália saw the smile on Adam's face as he spoke, and thought how odd it was, almost mocking as, if he did not consider himself worthy of such an honour. But had he not risked his life to venture behind enemy lines to rescue a fellow officer? How lightly he valued his existence!

'It is a great honour, *chefe*,' the boy gasped.

'Is it? A bullet or a sword-blade knows no rank. But, yes, it is an honour.' He eyes rested on Natália's down-bent head. In the flickering flames, her hair had an almost bluish sheen to it, and her skin was like burnished copper. Bluntly he said, 'I have nothing to offer you, *moça*.'

Natália caught her breath. Was he intimating that he wanted her to go with him? Slowly she raised her head, her long fingers still stroking the kitten now curled up in her lap, purring contentedly. He should have been happy, wanting to celebrate at his good news, but she saw only a great sadness in his eyes, and heard the loneliness in his voice.

'You have yourself. A small part, at least. What more can someone like myself ask of a great soldier?'

'Love.' The word was harsh with pain, and she felt herself flush. Was she the cause of this bitterness and anguish? Why? If he did not care for his wife, the wife he had abandoned seemingly without a second thought, why did he need to seek solace with another woman? What devil haunted him?

'I do not ask for something that cannot be mine. You gave it all to her, didn't you? The woman you married.'

'Perhaps I should cut out someone's tongue,' Adam muttered, and Nuno hurriedly faded into the shadows with his master's horse. Again those pale eyes dwelt on the girl in the firelight, and a strange gleam flickered in their depths. Without another word, he turned and strode off into the house.

How long Natália remained alone beside the dying fire she did not know. Off in the distance she could hear the cheeky chorus of crickets and bullfrogs along the river bank. These sounds intermingled with hushed voices and laughter from the darkness all round her. Suddenly she realised that if she did not take the initiative—risk Adam's anger and the very real chance of being recognised—she would lose him. Had she come all this way to sit alone with only a stray kitten for company?

Pilar's mouth gaped as she came into the kitchen clutching the animal to her breast.

'Take it.' She thrust it into the woman's hands as she began to rise from her chair, her brain still fogged with sleep. 'It needs a bath.'

'Where do you think you are going?' Pilar hissed, and Alída, who had fallen asleep on the sofa as she waited for Drew to return from a staff meeting, sat up to stare at them both curiously.

'Did I hear voices? Is Drew back?'

'No, only Adam,' Natália replied quietly, and went out before either of them could utter another word.

The candle had been snuffed. The only light in the room came from a shaft of bright moonlight falling through a high window over the bed. It was sufficient to reveal the shadowy figure reclining there.

'What have you done with your other stray?' Adam's voice came mockingly out of the darkness.

'I have left it outside.' She closed the door and stepped hesitantly to the bed. She could not see his face, only the outline of his long body. He had not undressed, yet she was sure he had expected her. Wanted her! He said nothing. He offered no word of encouragement as she slowly slipped out of her dress and sank down beside him. No endearment to put her at her ease. Had she really expected any? She was merely a servant-girl going to the bed of a handsome young man. He thought the worst of her, as he had of his wife. There was no trust in him, no real affection, for anyone except Drew, yet she sensed in him a great loneliness, a withdrawal from friends and family alike. He had never said he loved her at Alto Verde. It was she who had poured out her innermost feelings, and in doing so, rendered herself vulnerable to his wrath when he discovered she was already betrothed to another man. Why had he not listened to her for one moment?

And yet, what did the past matter now? She was where she belonged, in the bed of her husband. Whatever happened tomorrow or the day after, he would never be able to take that from her. This night was hers! Here, too, was her chance to be revenged on him for all his scornful taunts and hateful remarks, but she knew she could never bring herself to hurt him again. The first time she had been a foolish child who had unwittingly brought him pain. She must accept the small mercy God had granted her, and wish for no more.

'If you wish to stay with me, you will never again mention my wife. Do you understand, girl?' Adam said in a low tone. 'You have her eyes, but I forgive you that, for you are in no way like her. You are prepared to give everything, whereas she demanded everything of me —my very soul that I, Gold help me, was willing to give up to have her, but in return she gave nothing. Nothing, do you hear? She was the most beautiful creature I have ever met—and the most heartless.'

'Then you shall have my heart for what it is worth,' Natália whispered. She sought and found his hand, and touched it to her mouth. 'I shall make you forget her.'

'I want neither your pity nor your affection, *moça*. What we shall share will satisfy a need in us both, and has nothing to do with affection. To me you will always be *moça*. A face without a name, without a past. I want to know nothing about you, nor do I expect questions from you.'

'As you wish.' His hands began to explore her body, pushing away the last of her undergarments until they touched warm skin.

'You smell of Nuno's chicken,' he chuckled, and she gave an indignant little cry and would have pulled away from him, but he thrust his fingers into the mass of curls and tugged back her head, taking her lips with fierce, possessive ardour. For a moment Natália felt her whole body stiffen, resisting the natural desire to answer him, as memory of her wedding night rose in her mind. That was the one and only time he had ever touched her so intimately. She had begged him to make her his wife and he had pretended to accept her, only to toss her cruelly aside and sleep alone in the antechamber. She had cried herself to sleep that night, and so many afterwards that she had lost count.

'You have nothing to offer me. You are a child playing at being a woman. I would rather pay for my pleasures than bed you.'

He was certainly taking his revenge on her, with any woman who took his fancy. She would show him she was no child. She was all woman. His woman!

His mouth possessed hers for a moment longer before moving slowly, caressingly to her cheek, the lobe of an ear, neck and breasts until she moved beneath him restlessly. Her love, her loyalty, her body, belonged to him alone. How she prayed that one day he would realise it!

His lips moved back to hers, eager and waiting with a hunger that startled him. He gave a soft chuckle.

'So you are not the little innocent you would have me believe! No matter.'

Natália cried out as the room spun about her, closed her eyes and clung to him, caught up in a whirlpool of desire which seemed to have no end. She heard Adam call out a name, thrust her lips against his and held him tighter still as the world exploded.

Not until the early hours of the morning, when she awoke, did she remember that the name had been hers!

CHAPTER NINE

'WHAT IS IT? Can you not tell me what troubles you?'

As she felt Adam move restlessly beside her, Natália sat up. Outside the high window it was growing light. This was the fourth night he had gone without sleep. She had lain quiet while he tossed in the bed, or rose to find his *cigarrillos* and wander outside to sit alone and smoke. Once she had followed him, only to find Nuno crouching a few feet away, already protecting him in his own way that shut out everyone else. Adam was unaware of either of them as he stared off into the darkness, and she crept back to the room without a word.

Two weeks of lying beside him at night, making love, coming to know the soldier who had seen death—at times invited it with his daring acts of bravery, especially when one of his comrades was in danger—as well as the man who brooded on an incident in his past which he could not forget and would not share with anyone. Listening to his quiet voice coming to her out of the darkness, telling of battle stratagems, lost friends, the growing boredom of the English army encamped near by as they peered through gathering autumn mists and dreamed of a fight.

Never of himself. The Adam she had grown to know and love at Alto Verde was barred to her. The man who had spoken with such deep affection in his tone of his home, the vineyards, the *quinta* he one day hoped to have for his own never resurfaced. He was a stranger she must learn to love all over again. It was not difficult.

All his men were anxious to be back in the field, he

told her. In the north, after having, in July, captured the fortress of Ciudad Rodrigo from the British, the French commander Masséna was now preparing to hurl all his men into the capture of Portugal. But to achieve his aim, he must first turn his full attention to the second fortress which defended the road into Portugal—Almeida.

Natália had listened to the rumours, the speculation that the army would soon march to help in the defence of the inhabitants of the garrison there, and had prepared herself to follow her man, but Wellington had given no such order. No men were sent to block Masséna's path, although as well as the many stationed at Sobral, there were fighting units and cannon on the fortified heights above the River Alva who could have moved swiftly to effect a speedy attack.

No one understood why they sat about day after day, or engaged in needless drilling. What use was practice? They wanted the enemy before them, to avenge old scores. Yet few questioned their commander-in-chief. Natália had become aware that they trusted him implicitly, awaited his commands with a blind faith she found frightening. His judgment was never wrong, never contested.

'Almeida has fallen.'

'But everyone said how well guarded it was, and with enough provisions to last until help arrived—if the French attacked.'

'Or the rains bog Masséna's army into the mud,' Adam commented, realising she had already known of the town's surrender and had been waiting for him to break the news to her.

She asked no questions of his comings and goings, whether he was gone from the farmhouse for an hour or a day, but she was always well informed as to what was going on. Nuno had told him how she went down to the river and sat with the women, not joining in their often bawdy conversations but sitting to one side of them, listening to all the latest gossip, and the latest news, gained from a great variety of sources.

She knew everything that went on about them, but never once, since they had first come together, had he been subjected to the slightest inquisitiveness on her part. As soon as he retired to his room for the night, no matter at what hour, she would come to him and remain until it grew light. Then she would dress and leave him. When he reached out in the night for her, she was always there, always ready to try to please him. During the day he hardly ever saw her. He found himself beginning to look for those dusky features and being disappointed when he did not see them.

He would never trust another woman, let alone love one and render himself vulnerable again to the hell he had endured that short time with Natália. He had loved her. That was the bitterest pill of all to swallow. He, who had remained out of reach of all the eligible women who had wanted him, had been taken in by a pair of bright blue eyes and a shy smile! Now he was forced to admit, albeit grudgingly, that he had begun to care for the girl at his side. There was a bond between them he could not define with words, and he did not comprehend how she had succeeded in pushing aside the barriers he had erected about himself, and entering his solitary existence to share his pain and bitterness, without him being aware of the intrusion.

But she was there whenever he needed her. Night after night, when nightmares haunted him, her cool hands were on him soothingly, her soft lips against his cheek. She gave herself, and asked nothing in return. He had given her his protection for as long as she wished it—a small thing in return for such unselfishness. Would he have given even that if she had not possessed Natália's eyes? When he made love, it was not to the girl with no name, but to his wife, whose name came often—unknowingly—to his lips as he slept.

More so now, since her arrival.

She snuggled close against him as he slipped an arm about her shoulders and drew her down to him again. At the bottom of the bed, the kitten she had adopted, fatter now and clean, watched them through sleepy yellow eyes and yawned. What would happen to these two when the army moved out? It was inevitable now! There had to be a battle before much longer, or else Masséna's army would gain too strong a foothold in the mountains.

So far, the bands of *guerrilleros* he and his fellow officers had trained, together with the Ordinança, were causing havoc in the Beira Mountains, killing French stragglers without mercy in retaliation for their own ill-treatment at the hands of the enemy, and Wellington's scorched-earth policy had laid bare most of the countryside. The French would not be advancing on full stomachs despite the three hundred and fifty thousand pounds of bread they had discovered when Almeida was turned over to them.

The Ordinança were Portuguese peasants, armed with an assortment of ancient, but frightening weapons from blunderbusses to the wooden quince-poles used for knocking down fruit, and as effective in rendering a man insensible or killing him as any sword or pistol. They wore no uniforms, but dressed in traditional style, sporting woollen caps, breeches and stout boots. Under ancient Portuguese law, they had always been called on in times of emergency. The French, however, considered them as they did the *guerrilleros*, little more than rebellious peasants, and prisoners were hung from the trees without trial or ceremony.

Almeida had been a disaster, Adam thought, that not even Wellington for all his brilliant mind could have conceived. A French shell, landing before the cathedral, which was used by the British as a powder arsenal, had struck gunpowder leaking from one of the kegs being carried outside. The powder ignited, and the cathedral, the castle and a good part of the town were obliterated in a devastating explosion. Hundreds of the garrison perished in the disaster, and the very next day, what was left of the town surrendered.

'Will there be a battle now?' Natália asked hesitantly.

'Soon, I'm sure.' Why did he have to sound as if it was what he wanted, she thought. Why did men always like to fight and play at soldiers? 'You will be safe here, but I have made provision for you in the unlikely event that the French reach Sobral. Long before then you will accompany Alída to Mafra—or perhaps to Lisboa. I have her promise.'

'I will not!' Natália twisted round in his arms to look up at the profile outlined above her. 'I shall come with you. You will need me.'

'I need you alive—not blown to pieces, moça. Be sensible,' Adam insisted. He did not know what he would do after the fight. He made no plans; he dared not. 'If you don't do as I say, I shall have you both taken to Mafra under guard. She, too, has some idiotic idea of following her husband to war. It is no game we play. You would not like what the French do to their prisoners . . . You have the added disadvantage of being a very pretty young woman.'

'If you are tired of me, then say so, and I shall leave tomorrow!' Natália blinked back angry tears. It was unthinkable that she should allow him to go without her. What if he were injured—or killed! No! Her prayers, and her love, would protect him. She had to believe they would bring him back to her.

But what then? She could not remain in her disguise in Mafra. The strain of pretending to be someone she was not was beginning to tell on her, even after this short time. And despite all the care she had taken with her skin, she was aware of it gradually beginning to lighten as the dye faded, and in her hair, when she subjected it to daily scrutiny, there were more and more reddish tints.

Pilar's limited supply of powders was running out too quickly. She wanted to be with Adam at all times, not just during the hours of darkness when the shadowy room protected her secret. Avoiding him during the day was becoming more difficult, and Alída's excuses for her absence less convincing.

Drew had been insisting, for days now, that she return to Mafra and take Alída with her. Like Adam, she suspected he knew more than he would tell. Both women stubbornly refused to budge, but Natália feared that her nights of happiness were numbered. To go now, before she was exposed and sent packing by the man she adored with every fibre of her being . . . There was no choice for her. She belonged at his side and there she would remain—with or without his approval.

'Say you will go to Mafra, moça,' Adam said in a gentle tone. 'I'll not part with you in this manner.'

His words chilled her. He was leaving!

'When?' Somehow she forced the single word to her lips.

'At first light. My men and I are ordered to Gouveia to await the arrival of Wellington.'

'But his headquarters are at Celorico . . . He is retreating while Masséna advances . . .' Natália began and heard Adam sigh.

'Within the Linhas de Torres Vedras we have a fortress that is stronger and more possible to defend than any other. Over one hundred forts with trained men to defend them. Four hundred cannon situated at strategic points. He knows what he is doing, moça. If my guess is correct, the French do not even realise what is waiting for them. Like a fly into the spider's web, they will come unsuspecting . . .'

'And you will have the chance to fight. It's all you have been waiting for—all of you!' she cried.

'It is not all I want, exasperating creature,' Adam

muttered, burying his lips against the smooth hollow of her throat. 'I want you!'

'I want you to stay and guard the women, Nuno. I can spare no other man for the task,' Adam said quietly, and caught the look of disappointment which flashed across the boy's face before he masked his utter lack of comprehension at the order. Even the fact he had been chosen to do a man's job did not ease the momentary pain. 'They are not to follow us, do you understand me? If they attempt it, you are to see them escorted to Mafra, where they will remain until Captain Sorrell and I return.'

'*Sim, chefe.* Am I not to follow you at all? Who will polish your saddle? Brush your uniform, steal your food?'

'I am capable of looking after myself, but I thank you for your concern. I am lucky to have someone who cares about me.'

'She does . . . the one with the bright eyes.' Nuno lowered his gaze as Adam turned from checking the contents of his saddlebags and stared at him from beneath arched bows.

'Does she now? And when did you become an authority on women, especially her kind?'

'I see things . . . I see her look at you, and I see the way you look at her—and for her, whenever she is not about.' The boy gave a cheeky grin.

'You see too much! Fetch me some coffee if it is still hot,' Adam retorted gruffly, and Nuno ran back into the house. It was Natália who reappeared however, a steaming mug of coffee held in both hands. As she came quickly towards him in the half light, Adam was reminded of another morning when he had ridden away from a woman. More tears, he wondered? Entreaties to follow him? But her eyes were dry although tired and without their usual depth of colour which tore so at his heart-strings.

'I came to say goodbye. Do you mind?'

Worldlessly he shook his head and sipped at the hot liquid. He had talked half the night, and needed something to revive him at this unearthly hour. His men were assembling not far away, as always anxious to be moving back into the line of battle. How soon, he wondered? A few days? A week?

'I wish I had something to give you. A keepsake—a talisman to bring you back safely,' she whispered through trembling lips. She was close to tears, but she contained them. She had to be strong, or risk blurting out the truth here and now. 'But I have given you all I have.'

'I know.' The gentleness in his voice touched her. For a moment he allowed his fingers to dwell on the smooth curve of one cheek. His eyes never left her face. 'I shall not forget you, moça. From the very beginning you made that impossible. Come, kiss me goodbye before I relent and take you with me this very minute . . .'

Natália went eagerly into his arms, gaining comfort and courage from their strength. His mouth on hers silenced an entreaty to follow him when it was safe. There was an urgency, a desperation, in the long-drawn-out kiss which left her spent and breathless when she was released. The empty coffee mug was pressed into her limp grasp, and she was left standing weak-kneed and dazed as he flung himself into the saddle and rode quickly off to where his *guerrilleros* were gathered on the river bank. Many were also saying their last farewells.

As Natália neared the house, she saw Drew standing in the doorway, fastening the cuffs of his shirt. He had aged since the first day they met at Alto Verde, she thought, looking into the thin, tired face. She and Alída were an additional burden to the worries he already had on his mind, and now Adam was leaving again. Both were silently wondering if they would ever see him again, and praying that they would.

'We said our goodbyes last night,' he said quietly, answering her question before it was uttered. 'I thought the two of you would like to be alone this morning.'

'Thank you. That was kind—and thoughtful.' With a stifled sob she came to him and laid her head against his chest, unable to hold back her tears.

'I am so afraid for him, and for you. For days no one has talked of anything but a confrontation with the French.'

'Isn't that what we have been waiting for, all these months? Why we are here? Courage! Wellington knows what he is doing. Our lines will hold.'

'Everyone is so confident.'

'Would you have it otherwise?' Drew chided gently. 'You will see him again soon.'

'*Sim*, very soon,' Natália murmured, and he held her away from him with a frown.

'Adam told me you have promised to stay here and take care of Alída,' he said meaningfully.

'Nonsense! We are both coming with you. What better escort could we have?' Alída emerged from a side room, folding the clothes she had taken from the closet. 'You can take these too, Pilar,' she said to the woman following her. 'We shall travel light. Everything else can be packed and sent back to Mafra. Now.' She came and stood in front of her husband, and flashed a reassuring smile at her sister. 'Natália and I will not budge on this, Drew. We have come this far with you, and will go further. To the edge of the battlefield itself, if necessary. You promised me we would not be parted again. We shall not.'

'My promise did not include Natália,' he returned gravely. 'I shall have to answer to Adam if anything happens to her.'

'I have shared his bed, that is all,' Natália intervened.

'I am nothing to him, but I know I cannot continue with this deception much longer. A few weeks at the most. Pilar has a few powders with her which will help to darken my skin again before I leave, but I feel . . .' She shook her head, unable to put into words the strangeness of the feelings that had gripped her for the past day or two. 'Sometimes, when he looks at me, he says nothing, you understand. Surely, if he recognised me, he would send me away? But last night, he talked of Alto Verde . . . of the wife who had tricked him, betrayed him . . . and of his desire to be free of the past. Oh, Drew, every word was like a sword being turned in my heart, and I could say nothing! Never before has he mentioned it, and he forbade me to remind him he had ever had a wife.'

'Then he knows! He must!' Drew exclaimed.

'How could he? Look at her,' Alída protested. 'They were alone only once at Alto Verde. His impression of Natália is of a lady—a well-dressed, refined young woman—not a servant-girl with a dubious past. We have no right to take this time away from her. Are we not snatching every moment we can?'

'I don't like to remind you, but Adam swears he has no feelings whatsoever for Natália and never did,' Drew reminded her.

'That's why he was drunk for a week after leaving Alto Verde,' Alída retorted. 'Of course he cares for her, but he's as stubborn as a *burro*! He won't admit it, because, if he did, he might have to reconsider what happened there. That perhaps Natália had not intentionally deceived him. Had I been betrothed to Cesar, I would have done the same thing. The man was impossible. A lout!'

'Who is now a commissioned officer in the Portuguese army with his own command,' Drew said. Both women stared at him aghast.

It was Natália who found her voice first and managed

to stammer, 'He—he is not . . . here? He could not be!'

'He arrived yesterday. When the army moves, Captain Cesar João Ferreira Duarte will be accompanying it.'

Natália collapsed on the sofa with a gasp, her hands pressed against her mouth. Pilar sank beside her to offer comfort. Adam had not recognised her, for, as Alída had said, they had spent so little time together alone, but Cesar was a different matter. He had known her since childhood and was always visiting the *quinta*. He would know her at once, especially if she was at Adam's side. What then! She could imagine his delight at exposing her in revenge for the shame she had brought upon his head by her flirtation with another man—a total stranger!

Looking up at the two silent, apprehensive faces before her, she smiled bravely. Blue fire glowed in the depth of her eyes. The news had not dulled her will to fight for the man she loved.

'I shall just have to stay out of his way, won't I?' she said with a shrug of slim shoulders.

Alída hugged her. Drew said nothing. He was thinking that the battle about to be fought with the French was nothing to the one about to take place behind the scenes.

For over three weeks, Wellington did not move from his new headquarters at Gouveia, but stood fast while his intelligence services sent despatches back about Masséna's advance towards the capital. On the 17th of September, news came to him that the French commander was leading his men along the road through Viseu. Behind every rock his men were hampered by the sniping of the Ordinança, which added to the discomfort of marching on empty stomachs. For although many forages were made for food, the countryside had been stripped bare. Apart from a few insect-infested potatoes, there was nothing.

Natália understood the stratagem now. The enemy were marching hungrily—but confidently—towards their goal—Lisboa. No resistance, except for the Ordinança and sporadic attacks by roving bands of *guerrilleros*. One of those bands, she knew, was lead by Adam. Each night she knelt by the tiny figure of the Madonna she had brought with her and prayed for his safety. She cared nothing for herself any more, gave no thought to the danger she personally would be in when she followed the rest of the army. Her life was unimportant, so long as he lived.

The French advanced, and Wellington withdrew all his forces in their path, enticing them on; ordering his officers and men back from the fortified heights overlooking the River Alva to an equally strong position on a towering hog's back called Bussaco. Here he positioned over fifty thousand men, both English and Portuguese, and sixty cannon. Then he, too, moved, and relocated his headquarters in the walled convent of Bussaco. Surrounded by his staff, he awaited the arrival of Masséna. The patient spider awaiting the unsuspecting fly!

'Isn't it a beautiful view, Alída?' Natália said, gazing onwards towards the towering plateau where black and white windmills were outlined on the heights, their sails singing out a shrill tune which came to them on the early morning breeze. Early morning mists had dispersed, revealing heather-covered cliffs dotted with elegant pine trees, and spiky aloes stretched the whole length of the ridge. The summer sun had baked the earth, and hardened it so that clouds of dust rose from beneath their horses' hooves. It was not as pretty as Alto Verde, she decided, but it was an awe-inspiring sight. Was it here that Wellington would rout the French and send them packing?

They had camped the night before alongside the River

Mondego, where two years before, on the first of August 1808, Wellington had made his initial landing in Portugal with a small force of ten thousand men to help the Portuguese and Spanish nationalists. Natália had been too excited to sleep. She had lain awake, listening to the sound of the water near by, trying to calm the wild beating of her heart at the knowledge that the following day she would see Adam again. He was one of the privileged officers who shared Wellington's accommodation in the walled convent at Bussaco. She wondered if Drew had obtained the information by chance or had deliberately found out his whereabouts for her. He said nothing any longer about her presence with the army. He had accepted that her love for his brother was as strong, as indestructible, as that he shared with Alída. They had grown close since Adam's departure almost three weeks before, and now he was like a brother to her, caring little if it did raise a few eyebrows.

Had he guessed, she wondered? Or Alída, with her sharp eyes? Natália laid a hand over her abdomen, yet could feel no beat of life from within to tell her whether what she prayed for was true. A child growing inside her—Adam's son! Proof of her love. He would never believe her if she told him, of course. Better if she left him while the magic still lingered. She might never have her husband—but she would have his child to love, to remind her of how it had once been.

She knew she must leave soon. After the battle, she had decided, when she knew Adam was safe, then she would return home to the *quinta*. Perhaps—if she prayed hard enough—Adam might one day come to her . . . *sim*. When the English had routed the French, and Portugal was free, then she would go home.

They stumbled upon a small band of French skirmishers, who were returning behind their own lines after an unsuccessful attempt to steal food under cover of

dark, without warning. Natália's horse reared violently
as men rose from behind the rocks to the left of her, and
the whine of a musket ball as it passed close to her ear
made her scream in fear. They were traversing a narrow
defile at the base of the plateau, already in sight of the
English cannon and the riflemen placed on the lower
slopes—the two siters and Drew riding slightly ahead of
Pilar and Nuno, with two dozen cavalrymen behind
them. She heard Drew shout, but his words were lost in
the thunder of gunfire. Desperately she fought to retain
control of the frantic animal beneath her. As it reared
again, she was flung violently from the saddle against a
solid wall of rock with such force that she was rendered
half senseless. Through pain-filled eyes she saw Alída
reeling in the saddle, the front of her pale grey dress
covered with blood. Drew was shouting orders, his face
a mask of stunned disbelief as he thrust himself across his
wife's body to shield her. Natália saw his own body jerk
suddenly, tried to rise to run to them, but was knocked
to the ground as Nuno spurred his horse forward to give
assistance.

The noise and confusion were unbelievable . . . the
acrid smell of gunpowder filled her lungs, together with
the sickly smell of death. Drew's men flashed past where
she crouched, her hands over her ears, her eyes focused
on the spot where she had last seen her sister and Drew.
She could see neither of them now.

Silence. A last cry from somewhere beyond in the
rocks . . . a moan from one of the wounded English
cavalrymen who lay a few feet away from her. Even as
she stretched out a hand to see if she could help him, his
breathing stopped. Men were slipping and sliding from
the slopes above, and one helped her to her feet and
guided her to where Pilar sat on a rock, dabbing at a
bloody graze on one arm. She could not have stood
without his support.

'It's nothing, child, a scratch,' she assured Natália,

seeing the tremor in the fingers which gently touched the injured place.

'Alída . . .' Natália whispered, twisting round in the arms which still held her. 'She was hurt! I must go to her.'

'There's nothing you can do for your mistress now, girl.' The soldier's tone was as gentle as he could make it. He had seen too much death to be affected by the loss of two more lives—even if one was a woman—and he had no idea that the creature he held, shocked, dishevelled, biting back tears, was anything other than the servant-girl she appeared to be. 'She's in God's hands—her man, too.'

Nuno came into her blurred vision. The boy's face was streaked with blood and dirt. She caught at his arm with trembling fingers, and whispered pleadingly,

'Adão! Fetch Adão . . . Hurry!'

"Sim, senhora."

Natália did not hear his answer, for no sooner were the words out of her mouth than a blackness descended over her and she slumped unconscious in the arms which held her.

A bell tolling somewhere in the far distance . . . voices . . . hands gently probing her body. How she ached! Every part of her felt as if it was bruised. What had happened to her? And then it came flooding back, the tidal wave of painful memory. They were dead. Both of them! Alída and Drew! She struggled to sit up, but waves of nausea swept over her the moment she raised her head from the rough pillow. She did not know the man bending over her, but the face of the tall, silent man standing beside the window of the cell in which she lay brought more pain—and bitter-sweet memories which she knew now might never be repeated.

'How is she?' Adam asked, not moving from where he stood, feet slightly apart, arms folded over his chest.

Only Nuno and the *guerrilleros* close to him knew the terrible pain and loss he had suffered and by some magnificent effort kept locked behind an impassive mask as he accompanied the body of his brother back to the convent of Bussaco. They knew that, when the time was right, when he was alone, out of sight of prying eyes, he would give way to his grief.

'Remarkably well, considering the way she was thrown. Your man told me she went into the air like a rag doll. Bruises, of course, and a few grazes which I've cleaned. No concussion. She's lucky there.'

'Lucky!' The shrillness of Natália's tone brought the doctor's eyes instantly back to her face. Adam moved a step closer to the bed, staring down into her face, at the cheeks smudged with dirt where the tears had dried across them. There was a livid bruise on one temple, and both her knees and a section of her right leg were raw and bloody. '*They* are dead!'

'And shock. I'll leave something to make her sleep,' the doctor concluded matter-of-factly. 'Is there someone who can take care of her for a day or two, until this has passed? I take it that she was close to . . .'

'Yes, to a woman called Pilar. Thank you for your trouble.'

'Yes, quite . . .' The doctor threw him a sympathetic look as he left. After twenty years in the medical profession he still disliked being in the presence of the bereaved. They unnerved him. So many different ways to absorb one's grief. Hysteria—withdrawal—a refusal to acknowledge that a loved one was actually dead—he has seen them all. When this damned war was over, he decided, he would return to England and retire!

'Where are they?' Natália asked dully. She managed to sit up, despite the sharp pain along one side of her forehead, and swing her legs over the end of the cot.

'In the chapel.' Adam turned back to stare sightlessly

out of the window again. 'I told you to stay in Sobral. You gave me your word.'

'What does that matter now?' She wanted to scream at his calmness. There was not a trace of emotion on his face or in his voice. Had he no heart? His own brother was dead! 'I want to see—her. Please?'

'You could have stopped her coming. It was your place to stop her. You knew the dangers.' His tone was suddenly harsh and accusing, and she flinched as though he had struck her.

'That's not fair!' She had no strength to fight his anger. Her shoulders drooped, and she wiped away a tear which came unbidden to her eye. 'The day you left, she said to me, "I have come this far and will go further. To the edge of the battlefield itself, if necessary." There was no way of stopping her. She wanted to be with her husband. As I wanted to be with you.' He spun about at her words, pale flecks of yellow gleaming in the narrowed green eyes. 'If I was wrong, and you think I deserve your anger, then reprimand me later . . . not now, please, Let me go to her?'

In silence he went to the door to open it, and watched as she reeled towards him. He slipped a steadying hand beneath her elbow as she looked about to fall. They walked the whole length of a long cloistered pátio where the sun danced in dizzy patterns before her on the flagstones. It was high in the sky, she noticed, when she lifted her eyes to glance upwards for a moment, and quickly lowered them again as pain obscured her vision. How long had she been unconscious?

A cowled monk standing outside a door ahead of them opened it and stepped to one side as they approached. Natália's steps faltered on the threshold of the chapel. Firmly, but gently, Adam ushered her inside and then let her go. But she did not notice. Her eyes were instantly riveted on the two plain oak coffins side by side before the altar. A woman enveloped in a heavy black shawl knelt in prayer a few feet away. As if in a dream, Natália forced herself to look down into her sister's face. She almost cried with relief to see the skin unblemished. Not a sign of injury—no mark to mar her pretty face. It was as if she were asleep. She lay with her hands folded across her breasts, the skirts of her gown neatly arranged about her, all dust and grime brushed from the grey velvet. Wild flowers covered the bloody patch where the musket ball had entered, killing her instantly as it penetrated the heart.

'Bless you, Pilar,' she whispered huskily, dropping to her knees beside the other woman, knowing instinctively it was she who had devoted such care to these final preparations.

'Many's a time I've dressed her, and you . . . But I never dreamed . . .' Pilar fell to weeping, rocking to and fro on the cold hard stone. 'I can't bear to lose her . . . Only the other day she was telling me how happy she was . . . How good life was . . .'

'We must be thankful she found happiness—and the love of a brave, kind man who adored her,' she returned, taking Pilar in her arms, seeking comfort and reassurance from this one person who had always been there when she needed such things. But as sobs racked the woman's shoulders, she realised she had none left to give. The loss of Alída was as great for her as it was for Natália.

She rose, swaying, to her feet, and heard the sound of footsteps behind her as she bent and laid her lips against her sister's cold cheeks. At Alída's side, Drew looked composed and tranquil—at peace.

'Together,' she muttered, stretching out a hand to grip the sleeve that came into her view. 'They must always be together—as they were in life. They must not be separated . . .'

'They shall not.' Adam caught her as her knees began to buckle. She fought weakly against the arms which enfolded her and lifted her from the ground, wanting to stay with her sister until she was taken away to her final resting-place. They had shared so much that she did not want to be torn away so cruelly. 'Come, you need to rest. I shall make all the arrangements.'

When Natália awoke, the first thing she remembered was the warm milk Adam had made her drink when he returned her to bed. She knew by the languidness of her limbs that it had been doctored, probably with the sleeping potion left to calm her. It was still light outside, but she had no means of knowing what time it was or even if it was the same day. And there was no sign of Pilar. She found this strange.

Tentatively she stood up. She felt weak and disorientated, and there was an uncomfortable fluttering in her stomach which sent an icy chill of fear through her. Was she with child? Had the shock of her sister's death somehow damaged the life she carried inside her? She stood for a moment, long, slender fingers spread out over her stomach, hoping for some sign, but she felt only sick. Yet, was that in itself not a sign? God had shown her in this holy place that she carried Adam's son!

As she opened the door, Nuno leapt to his feet. He had been sprawled half-asleep across the entrance. The eyes which swept over her were amazingly alert, she thought, and searching. What was it she was trying to remember? It would not come . . . Something he had said to her. Although she could not remember it, the words had concerned her. Why should they? What could he say to her that would upset her?

'My sis——,' she began, and then, quickly correcting herself, 'my mistress . . . where is she?'

'In the ground, with her husband,' the boy returned. 'Shall I show you? Are you all right?'

Natália had reeled back against the door, a hand against her breast. Buried—without her there! How could Adam have been so heartless! Was this not proof that he did not know who she was? Surely if he had known she was his wife, he would have woken her for the final blessings before her sister and Drew were taken from her for ever. She touched a hand to her forehead and found it was burning fiercely. Did she have a fever? 'I shall take care of the arrangements,' he had told her—and he had. Was he just being kind, or exacting a venomous revenge on her for her deception, both here and at Alto Verde? Could any man be so cold—ruthless? Instinctively she knew that Adam was such a man. When hurt, he would strike back with any means in his power. She did not know what to think, or to believe, any more.

'Show me,' she whispered.

The single grave was in a quiet, sheltered corner of the convent gardens, beneath a large almond tree. Natália's eyes filled with tears as she bent and gathered up a handful of earth and slowly scattered it over the newly-dug mound. Someone, again Pilar, she suspected, had dropped wild cactus-blossoms, bright red and yellow canna blooms and orange-blossom to alleviate the starkness of the dark earth.

'Rest well, dear sister, and you, Drew. Be as happy together now as you were on earth. You are so lucky. What you have known and what you have now, no one can take from you,' she whispered.

Nuno's eyes challenging hers across the grave were the last thing she remembered.

'You little fool, why do you think I had you drugged?' Adam said, leaning over the bed, glaring with unconcealed anger into her tearful face. 'I didn't want you to suffer this. Do you enjoy inflicting pain upon yourself?'

'I am used to it.' Natália turned her face into the pillow and her voice was muffled. How desperately she wanted to reach up and bring his dark face down to hers, feel his lips crushing hers, making her forget the horror of death—of loss—of helplessness! He had been at her side when she recovered from her faint, and so had Pilar, who bathed her face with cool water and rocked her in her arms until the spasm of weeping had passed. They were lost to her, she must accept it . . . If she had not decided to leave Adam and return to her father, she knew she must do so now. Somehow she would have to tell him that Alída was dead. Would he care? Would he cry? She had never seen him shed a tear for anyone. Like Adam, he was a man able to control his emotions. How glad she was to be a weak woman who could cry and release the tumult inside her. 'I'm sorry you have done so much. *Muico obrigada.*'

The hand laid upon her shoulder was very gentle. Strong fingers caressed the smooth expanse of bare skin where her blouse had slipped down.

'It is time to show you there is more in this world than pain and fear—and death.' She stiffened as she felt the hardness of his body slide alongside hers on the narrow bed. What was he doing? Pilar was still in the room. She twisted round in his arms to find they were alone. He had removed his jacket and shirt and she could smell the manly aroma of sweat and also horses on his skin, but she did not mind. It was so wonderful to feel him against her again, the strength of him, the tender caresses, the teasing kisses beginning at the nape of her neck and creeping down to her shoulder, the rise of her breast, exposed now beneath his exploring fingers.

He had always been gentle with her, considerate of her needs as well as his own, but never so much as at this moment. His kisses, the hands which stroked, teased and inflamed her body were intended to rouse her as never before and in doing so, perhaps, make it possible for him to lose himself completely in the world they created whenever they made love. She knew a part of him was always withdrawn from her, locked away deep inside him, that his satisfaction was never as great as her own.

His lips swept her skin, sending shivers of pleasure up and down her spine and clearing away the moment of shame she felt for being so happy when her sister was not yet cold in her grave. Alída was still the lucky one, for she and Drew would never be separated again. How soon would it be before Adam left her again? A day? Two? How long before she turned her back on him and the life she had been leading these past weeks to return home? Time and time again she went back on her decision to leave, while each time he touched her she wavered and decided to stay. But in the morning, when she looked at her reflection, she knew that the masquerade could not continue indefinitely.

With a stifled sob she slid her arms about his neck and held him close to her.

'Love me, Adão,' she begged. 'Love me as though there were no tomorrow.'

Natália was still sleeping when Adam drew away from her and quietly dressed. Wellington was to inspect the outposts that morning, and he wanted to ensure that his men were good and ready. The fight was near, he could feel it, and his senses quickened at the thought of going into battle again, revenging himself on the French who had taken his brother's life.

As he turned to leave, he paused, struck by Natália's peaceful face. She lay on her side, the covers thrown back, one arm pillowing her head. They had shared something wonderful, quite unlike anything he had known with any other woman, and he knew he still loved her. Lightly brushing the hair from her cheek—how it had grown in a few short weeks!—his fingers lingered near a red-gold strand against her temple before he bent and gently touched his lips to hers. As he eased the bed-covers over her body, he realised that the smooth, golden patch of skin between the hollow of her breasts, which he had first noticed at the camp at Sobral, was no longer there.

CHAPTER TEN

At Adam's own request, he had been allowed to place his men along the lower slopes of the huge mountain among the Portuguese riflemen who were also placed under his immediate command. He arrived at their positions to find that a skirmish had taken place a few hours earlier under cover of the thick fog which blanketed the whole area. Two of his men and several of the Portuguese Caçadores further along the line had been wounded, but the French had been driven back, and they would not have had time to assess the strength of their opponents, he surmised, as he climbed to a higher vantage-point in the hope of seeing the landscape better.

He could not even discover where his own men lay in the deep heather or behind huge needle-pointed aloes. The night before, the many bivouac fires of the enemy could be clearly seen, but now the mist obscured everything. There was an eerie silence. He felt as if nothing existed except him, yet he knew Masséna had over sixty thousand men assembled, some less than three miles away. His own intelligence scouts had reported two near-by villages occupied. San Antonio de Cantaro, from where the French had a good look at Wellington's command-post, high on the hills outside the convent, and Moura, on Bussaco's north-eastern slopes. Good positions, Adam mused, held by crack troops, but to get at the English they had to climb the mountain. This, in his opinion, placed them at an immediate disadvantage.

When he returned, Nuno brought him a mug of hot coffee and unwrapped the bundle he had brought with him—fresh *queijo de manhã*, thick round cheeses made of goat's milk, and wedges of still warm bread.

'You have not eaten,' he said, as Adam shook his head.

'I am not hungry just now.' He did not like the waiting which always preceded a battle. He did not want time to think, to remember, to make plans he might not be alive to implement. 'Pass the word along that there will be no fires tonight, so the men should eat heartily while they can. And no wine after dark. I don't want the French stepping over them while they sleep.'

Finishing his coffee, he got to his feet, pulling the collar of his coat high about his neck as he walked to his horse. This damned mist chilled him to the bone! He needed to be alone, to rid his mind of the tantalising memory of the sleeping girl he had left. No other thoughts must remain but those of what was soon to happen—the preparations for battle and the welfare of his men.

'Have my uniform ready for the morning. When the time comes, I shall lead my brother's men too.' Four good men had also died in the ambush that had claimed Drew and Alída, and he knew Drew's men were as eager as himself to even the score. 'I'll be back before long.'

'Shall I ride with you?' There was a sudden tightness about the firm mouth, a hardness in the eyes, which made Nuno's feeling of uneasiness grow.

'No, *moço*. Go and steal a chicken for when I return,' Adam ordered with a faint smile.

For once, matching his wits against the eagle eyes of the cook was the last thing the boy wanted to do. He had heard, although Adam had said nothing, that there was a certain Portuguese officer by the name of Cesar Duarte in command of the troops on the heights above them. A loud-mouthed braggart, by all accounts, who drank too much *aguardente* and spoke out of turn. In two short days he had earned the dislike of his men and fellow officers alike.

It was inevitable that Adam should meet him. This

particular area was under his command, made up of
riflemen from his own band of *guerrilleros*, infantrymen,
and, on the heights, cannon trained on the winding cart
track from San Antonio where General Reynier's
Second Division were entrenched. He was talking with
other officers on the ridge when another man joined
them. Out of the corner of his eye Adam glimpsed the
grey uniform, lavishly trimmed with gold, which the
Portuguese officers wore, and a moustachioed face
which rang a warning bell deep in the recesses of his
mind, but it was not until he turned to be formally
introduced that he fully recognised the newcomer.

'Major Sorrell and I already know each other,' Cesar
interrupted rudely before the young Lieutenant could
complete the formalities. He reddened and coughed as
Adam's eyes narrowed to green diamond points. Without realising it, his hand dropped instinctively to the
pistol in his belt. The look Cesar gave him was derisive,
the dark eyes contemptuous, as they swept over the
other man's irregular mode of dress. He looked like a
common peasant instead of an English officer. And this
was the man who had stolen Natália from him! She had
lain with him in the fields like a whore, but had repulsed
his advances—and he had been betrothed to her. She
had belonged to him! A red mist of hate swam before his
vision. He heard Adam mutter something to his companions, and turn away without even so much as a nod to
acknowledge him.

'*Sim*, I know the Major very well,' he said in a loud
voice. 'His appearance bears out what I thought of him
when we first met. A low-born peasant with the manners
of a pig!'

Adam came to an abrupt halt and spun about on his
heel. A man who knew him well, had ridden with him
many times over the years, laid a warning hand upon his
arm, but it was shrugged off. There was murder blazing
in the eyes which seared Cesar's face, but his hatred was

so overwhelming that he was spurred on to more insults, more innuendos, heedless of the cost!

'Shall I tell you gentlemen about this cur who masquerades as a fine English gentleman? His eyes alighted on the daughter of a certain wealthy landowner who out of the goodness of his heart had offered the hospitality of his home. She was betrothed to me, senhores. Our wedding date was fixed. And this, this . . .'—he uttered a foul Portuguese expletive that Adam had only ever heard before from fishermen in Lisboa—'seduced her one night. Deprived her of her innocence and then the following morning rode away, deserting her.'

'You seem to have forgotten one important fact, my foolish friend.' Adam's voice was very quiet. Perfectly calm, without anger. The men near by exchanged knowing looks. There had to be a challenge! Adam Sorrell was not one to turn his back on such insults. 'Natália is my wife.'

Not until he had uttered the words did he realise that they might not be true. He had asked—no, demanded —that his father arrange an immediate annulment of the farcical marriage. The last letter he had written regarding the subject had not yet been answered. Close on its heels would be the news of Drew's death. He hoped one would soften the terrible blow of the other.

'So. You are a coward as well as seducer of women! I hear you have a gipsy girl in your bed now. Who did you steal her from?' Cesar's sibilant hiss broke the thin wedge of Adam's composure.

His hand lashed out and struck Cesar across one cheek. Then, with great deliberation, he drew it back and delivered a second blow. Not the usual light slap that custom demanded, but one intended to insult and inflict pain—which they did. Cesar's head snapped back, and blood seeped from a split lower lip.

'At the moment I have more important things on my mind than killing you, senhor, but rest assured that when our business here is finished, and if you have not been despatched by some lucky Frenchman, I shall have the pleasure of seeing you on the end of my blade. My seconds will call on you to arrange the time and place. The weapons will be sabres. I shall pray that the French do not deprive me of our meeting. I bid you good morning, gentlemen.' Adam nodded briefly to the silent cluster of men who had gathered to watch and listen and speculate on the outcome of the encounter, mounted his horse, and rode away without a backward glance.

The whole incident had taken less than five minutes, but it kept the entire encampment in conversation for the rest of the day and well into the night. Adam Sorrell a married man, and him the most eligible bachelor about! Well, that was what everyone had thought! Sly devil! As tight as a drum, that one. The Portuguese was a dead man, of course. Sabres were the Major's weapon, and no one could best him!

Nuno was in full possession of all the details from one of the women who brought them food around mid-day —a full hour before Adam returned. He was bursting with questions, but the sight of Adam's taut features and pale glittering eyes deterred them. Quickly he fetched a mug of hot coffee and took the horse away to water and feed. When he returned, Adam was sprawled beside the fire, the coffee still untouched. He seemed unaware of his surroundings or the many curious glances cast at him by his men.

The boy fanned the fading embers for a moment with an olive branch before tossing several large potatoes into the grey ashes. He again unwrapped the bundle containing the *queijo de manhã* and the bread, and presented it to Adam. This time it was accepted, but with a nod only. His thoughts were elsewhere, Nuno realised, as he returned to the fire and began to roast the chicken he had stolen earlier. He had almost been caught coming out of the cook's supply tent, and that had worried him. He was growing soft! He had no reason to steal when Adam provided money to buy everything—but how he loved to resort to his old ways and prove what an adept little thief he was! There was no one better in the whole camp. Why, even soldiers came to him, and some women, too, wanting perfume, soap, or little things to please their men. He had grown quite rich from their needs. He knew Adam would not approve of his sideline and so he said nothing, yet there were times when he thought his master knew everything he did.

He needed to be distracted, the boy thought, sending a thoughtful look over his shoulder at the silent man. He had not uttered a word since he returned. He was not afraid of Cesar Duarte—then what? Of being killed in battle, perhaps, and never seeing *her* again? Why then did he not tell her he knew?

After a moment he began to whistle softly to himself as he prodded the plump chicken, remembering how he had once shared one with the girl. She was clever, that one, and had ensnared the lion—but how long could she keep him before he wished to be free of his cage?

Adam's head jerked up as the boy began to sing in a husky, off-key voice. His eyes narrowed sharply as he saw his sergeant Julío and some of his men who were seated nearby, cleaning their weapons, exchange grins and quickly avert their gaze as he looked their way.

'What is that nonsense you are singing?' he growled.

'A riddle of life, *chefe*,' the boy laughed cheekily.

> 'I took a woman to be my wife.
> She was nothing but trouble and strife.
> I ran away—she followed me.
> Now we live in harmony.'

'Have you been at my brandy again? Give me some coffee if it's hot.'

'Don't you like riddles, *chefe*?' Nuno's grin was wicked as he brought Adam another mug of steaming coffee, black and unsweetened as he liked it. Perhaps he should have ladled some sugar into it, he thought, as a sour look greeted it. 'I thought you ought to know . . .'

'Did you think I wouldn't recognise my own wife?' Adam interrupted, lowering his voice so that it did not carry beyond the two of them. 'I knew her at once. It suits me to play her game, that's all.'

It was a lie, but fierce pride forbade that he should admit it had been almost a week before he had accepted the incredible truth—that the dark-skinned creature who crept into his bed each night was really his wife —the woman he had married and rejected in the space of one short day! Loved and hated without ever truly knowing her.

He knew her now. Every delight of her young body, the softness of it, the magic that was for him alone. She had come to him as a virgin, untouched by any other man, and the moment of discovery as he entered her for the first time had overwhelmed him, and brought to mind the terrible accusations he had heaped on her head at Alto Verde. His abandonment of her on their wedding night and subsequent rejection of her the following morning. Had he not been so angry, so hurt, he would have known then . . .

Why had she followed him? So many possibilities haunted him as he lay beside her. Seeking revenge for his actions on those two shameful occasions? Perhaps the deception was intended for one purpose only—to get herself with child and so fulfil her father's dream. If only he could believe, and accept without reservations, the silent promises her body made each time it touched his.

'*Chefe*, do you want more coffee?' Nuno asked for the second time.

Adam shook his head and handed back his empty mug. This was no time to think of her—or the past—or the future. He might not have one.

He was angry that Nuno had also recognised her and made it known, for it forced him to accept his responsibilities towards her. Dubious as he was as to her reasons for following him, she had placed herself in danger and he must try to ensure her safety. He could not just leave her to fend for herself.

'If anything happens to me, *moço*, you are to take her back to Alto Verde. You will find ample money in my pack back at the convent. And take anything else you need,' Adam told him quietly. 'Tell her . . . Well, you will think of something if it comes to it.'

What words were explicit enough to say what was in his heart? Had been there since the first moment he saw her. Had withered and almost died in the long weeks of separation when he had dwelt in his own personal hell, believing her to be nothing less than a little tramp, only to be reawakened, nurtured, intensified by the blissful hours she had spent in his arms.

Whatever she was, whatever her reasons for being at his side, he loved her, and wanted her so much his body ached, but he was sure that, if he returned to her that evening, he would have to know the truth. Were her motives purely selfish, or had she been driven to a reckless, unthinking act by the same fires of passion which had consumed them both that fateful night at Alto Verde? Perhaps he would never know.

Nuno felt uneasy. He talked as if he might not survive the coming battle. That was not his way!

'Tell her yourself—afterwards,' he answered, putting away the remnants of bread and cheese. 'You are not going back to the convent tonight?' Like most of the men, he had heard the rumours of a dawn attack.

'No, I shall stay here. There is much to be done.'

'A letter?' Natália stared at the envelope held out to her. No one except Adam's father knew where she was. The soldier who had been told to deliver it had heard of the dark-skinned beauty Major Sorrell had for a bedmate, and also that she was not too bright.

Patiently he said, 'The letter is for your mistress, but she's dead, isn't she, so you had best give it to the Major when he returns. *Comprendo?*'

'*Sim*. We understand.' Pilar came forward to take the envelope and usher him out of the room. 'It is from Lisboa.'

'Then it must be from the Senhor Charles!' Natália's fingers trembled slightly as she tore at the envelope and extracted a single piece of paper. The bold neat handwriting leapt up at her, and she gave a cry of distress. 'Papa is ill! Listen, Pilar.'

> Dearest Alída and Natália.
>
> Your last letter was most welcome, telling me you are all well. I wish in return I could write words of good news, but alas, I have to tell you that on my visit to your father at Alto Verde last week, he collapsed and was immediately put to bed, where he has remained ever since. The doctor is concerned for his health, my dears. I implore one or both of you to return home and be with him. He is an old, sick man who desperately needs you. *Believe me, he does.* (These last words were heavily underlined.) God protect you all until we are together again—all of us!
>
> Charles Sorrell.

Natália clutched the paper to her breast. Ill, perhaps dying—and no one there to care for him! The years of being neglected and ignored seemed unimportant in the face of the knowledge that her father needed her, at last! 'I must leave, and go to him!' As soon as the words were uttered, she knew what she had said. The decision had been made for her. She no longer had a choice whether to go or stay. 'Gather together our things, but keep them out of sight, Pilar. Adam must know nothing of this.'

'Be brave, *menina*,' the woman said, squeezing her arm reassuringly. 'God will watch over them both.'

'We shall leave first thing tomorrow morning. There are always wagons going back to Mafra. I shall take a horse from there, and you can follow in the carriage. It will be more comfortable for you.'

'I will not,' Pilar said with an indignant snort. 'You are not travelling through the countryside alone and unprotected. We've come this far together, and you'll not separate us now. I may break every bone in my body, but we ride together!'

It was late that evening before Natália realised that Adam was not coming back to the convent. When he did, she would be gone from his life, perhaps for ever. There was nothing she could do any more, and perhaps it was for the best. She knew she might well have given herself away, had he come to her and they had made love as they did the night before. It had been so perfect, so fulfilling. A memory to last for ever.

Poor Charles, she thought, remembering the warmth contained in the short letter. In a few days he, too, would receive the sad news of Drew's death. She would write as soon as she reached Alto Verde and invite him to stay at the *quinta*. They had become good friends in the short time they had known each other, and she had so much to tell him. Perhaps he would find consolation in her company, as she knew she would in his.

She was leaving so many people she loved. Drew and Alída lying close together beneath the almond tree. She prayed that in spring the white and pink blossom would gently fall upon their resting-place, a carpet of soft silky petals for the two ill-fated lovers. Adam—he might miss her for a day or two, but he was a soldier who could occupy his mind with many things. Besides, there would be other women eager to share his bed once they knew she had gone. Would he let them? Would his arms hold another, his lips tease and inflame the heart of some camp-follower—a lady in Lisboa perhaps, anxious to welcome the victorious English officer?

The British had to win, of course. She could not envisage defeat, for it would mean that the roads were open for the French to march all the way to Lisboa. She shuddered and crossed her arms about her body, wishing Adam were beside her on the narrow bed. The thick convent walls shut out the sounds of activity outside, and at long last she slept.

The attack came at dawn, as many had anticipated. Skirmishes at first on the lower slopes between the Portuguese Caçadores and French infiltrators, then, through the heavy mist which once again obscured the mountain, four enemy battalions began to advance upon Bussaco.

Natália heard the sound of cannon booming through the stillness and leapt from the bed. Pilar ran after her as she flung open the door and ran barefoot out into the cloisters, vainly trying to wrap a shawl about her shoulders. The mist was heaviest about the convent walls, for it was high on the hill, but it did not deaden the ominous sound. It was fire from Wellington's command-post, she realised, blasting the attackers with grape and canister. A horrible way to die! Many would—on both sides, before the day was over. How could she leave now? Yet to linger . . .

'Come back; there is nothing we can do yet.' Pilar wrapped the woollen' shawl about her shivering shoulders and guided her back inside.

'Later,' Natália murmured. '*Sim*. Later, they will be bringing back the wounded . . . They will need help.'

Pilar cast her a worried look. Had she forgotten about the father who lay ill at Alto Verde? She was going to remind her, but then quickly turned away. The conflict on Natália's face was tearing her apart. Go or stay?

Either way she might lose one of them! On her way to find food for them both, Pilar knelt at the back of the chapel and prayed as she had never prayed before. The cannon continued to thunder, but she was oblivious to the noise.

Situated along the narrow cart track along which the French commander General Reynier was to launch an attack behind the British, and try to cut Wellington off from the rear, Adam's *guerrilleros* and the Portuguese artillery hammered unmercifully at the approaching men. Time and time again they were driven back, time and time again the French gained another foothold —another inch—fell back. Some held, many died, in the withering fire from the slopes and the heights above.

The whole length and breadth of Bussaco ridge echoed with cannon fire, the screams and moans of the dying and injured. It was one of the bloodiest battles to be fought of the whole war. Both sides had gauged the strategic necessity to hold this particular area. They fought on the slopes, in the dense bushes and scrub, were torn on needle-sharp cacti and aloes, blasted with grapeshot, cut down by musket fire. In one short hour, with fog still prevailing, the carnage was devastating.

Seeing the tide of men climbing relentlessly towards his position, Adam rallied his *guerrilleros*, who mounted their horses and charged down the hill, sweeping all before them to one side, fighting hand to hand when horses fell beneath them. When his own horse was brought down by fire, he leapt from the back of the dead animal, as much incensed by its death as by that of his brother, or by the sight of Julío—not only the leader of his *guerrilleros*, but a friend—felled in front of him, nearly sliced in half by a sabre.

He fought like a man possessed—a demon driven on by hatred and deep-rooted emotions he was not even aware had come to the surface to rally him again and again to urge his men on—to drive the enemy from the slopes and make their position safe. He succeeded, but the cost was appalling. Half of his men dead, another dozen critically wounded.

As Adam was climbing back to safety, a man rose out of the shrub above him, a pistol levelled directly in his face. For a moment he was transfixed with shock. Had the fool lost his mind? He wore a Portuguese uniform —could he not see Adam's was English?—and then behind the lethal barrel he glimpsed the hate-filled eyes of Cesar Duarte and was suddenly seized with a wild desire to laugh. Had he just survived the dreadful fighting below to be cut down by a man supposedly fighting on his own side?

She would never know he loved her! The thought screamed through his brain as he saw Cesar's finger grow white about the trigger. Instinct hurled him sideways. At the same time as Nuno rose from the boulder where he had been hiding and shot Cesar at point-blank range, a wounded Frenchman some yards away discharged his musket into Adam's back. Both men fell simultaneously to the ground, two more victims of the storm which raged about them . . . unnoticed except by the slight figure of the young boy who scrambled wildly down towards his fallen friend.

Natália was exhausted, but she would not allow herself to rest and so to dwell on what was happening beyond the convent walls. As soon as the first wounded were brought in, she fell to the task of helping the monks to bring them inside the walls, into spare rooms, out-houses, to lay them even on the hard ground until they could be attended to by the doctors. Many died where they lay before they could be attended to. Others begged for water, and thrashed madly on straw pallets, cursing the limbs which caused them so much pain, not knowing they were no longer there. She spent hours making bandages, fetching and carrying with the other women, falling naturally into the part that all women take when caught up in the mêlée of war. Nurse, servant, friend, comforter, mother, sister, sweetheart. Something to everyone in need, and knowing deep in her heart that the very person to whom she wanted so dearly to do and to be all these things might well be lying out in the hills, dead or wounded.

Throughout the day the sound of cannon fire continued. Sometimes the volleys of musket fire seemed quite close, at others, far in the distance. Outside the convent, the loss of life on both sides was apparent to all as the mists began to dispel and English and French took their first good look at the results of their encounters.

Wellington had held the heights of Bussaco. Elsewhere, regiments of English fought alongside Irish, Scottish Highlanders beside Portuguese musketeers, whose withering fire that day was to bring them great renown. At times often outnumbered, these men held their positions, gave ground only when ordered and then often refought hard and long to retake it.

In his grey great-coat and cocked that, without the usual colourful plumes that most commanders wore, a favourite target of enemy snipers, Wellington instilled continual confidence in his men with his clear, decisive orders. Suddenly through the raging noise was heard General Craufurd's great voice, 'Avenge Sir John Moore! Forward the Fifty-Second!' The death of that brave soldier, never forgotten, at the hands of the French at Corunna in the early stages of the war was avenged many times before the day was over.

'Are you *A Moça?*' Natália looked up from the side of the wounded man she was tending into the tired face of a woman wearing a blood-streaked apron over a dress soaked with sweat. The odour about her was nauseous, the odour of death . . . Mutely she nodded. 'Thought so! The boy Nuno said to find you. Your man's just been brought in—Major Sorrell. They'll be finished with him in a while, if you're interested.'

'Interested?' Natália came to her feet like a sleep-walker. 'Is . . . he . . . dead?'

'Did I say that? Lord, girl you look as if you are about to faint. You'll be no use to them—or him—if you do. Go outside and get some air, then find the surgeon's tent, the one nearest the shrine of the Virgin. You'll find him there.' The woman was the common-law wife of an English soldier who had been with him from the beginning of the conflict. Her young son, a drummer-boy in the regiment, had been killed when the French stormed up the slopes towards Wellington's command-post. Of her husband, she had no news. For a moment the lined face softened and she laid a hand on Natália's shoulder. 'He's safe now, child. They are evacuating the wounded back behind the lines at first light tomorrow.'

As Natália began to mumble her thanks, the woman turned away and was lost in the bustle surrounding them. She looked for Pilar, but when she could not see her, quickly threaded her way through the mass of bodies on the floor, shutting her ears to the pleading voices which tried to detain her, and went outside. It was dark! She blinked up at the star-laden sky almost stupidly. Where had the day gone?

She stood for a while gulping in mouthfuls of clean, fresh air. The ground as far as she could see was littered with bodies—French wounded as well as English. So many, and some so young. She experienced a moment of fleeting compassion as she stepped over one injured boy, not aged more than eighteen. His wounds were so dreadful that she could not feel hatred for him even though he was one of the enemy.

Her breath caught in her throat as she found the surgeon's tent, and she scanned the rows of faces out-side. Many would die of their injuries before morning, she realised. An orderly passed her, carrying a basket filled with amputated limbs, and she quickly covered her mouth with her hands to hold back the nausea. At Alto Verde she had seen death and destruction, had witnessed the villagers exacting their own brand of revenge on the enemy, but this . . . This was war as she had never seen it. War like this had never existed, even in her mind. Never could she have envisaged anything so terrible—so grotesque! All this to free her country from Napoleon's yoke. It was a high price. Never would her people be able to repay what had been done for them!

'Here, senhora!' Nuno came to his feet to guide her to where Adam lay. 'Over here.'

She fell on her knees beside the still figure who was half covered with the remnants of his bloodstained jacket. His shirt and underclothes had been removed, and his chest was swathed in bandages. He was so still! Natália laid trembling fingers against the thick covering, and almost wept at the slow beat of life which throbbed beneath her fingers.

'He is drugged, senhora. Thank God, the surgeon attended to him before they ran out of everything. Some of these poor devils will scream all night because there is nothing to kill their pain. I doubt if half of them will survive the journey back,' Nuno muttered. She saw he was holding tightly to one of Adam's hands—clinging like a child to the only man who had ever shown him kindness and affection.

Senhora! Now she remembered—he had called her that the day Drew and Alída died. *He* knew who she was! As realisation dawned on her face, the boy said quickly,

'You will stay with him? I have to find food, and brandy.'

'He needs soup . . . something light,' she protested, knowing he meant well.

'When the pain comes back, tonight or in the

morning, he will want something stronger than soup. You will not leave him?'

'Do you think I came all this way to desert him when he needs me most?' Natália replied softly. A faint smile flashed across the boy's dust-streaked features. In silence he acknowledged who—and what—she was, and relinquished his precious charge into her hands.

'Adão! Oh, *meu amor*, please don't die! I love you so much,' she whispered, settling herself at his side. The night air was chill, and she pulled the jacket high beneath Adam's chin. He did not stir as she gently wiped the dirt and grime from his face and fetched cool water to trickle between his dry lips. Despite the cold, his features soon became covered with a film of perspiration, and she knew a fever was raging inside him.

Not until Nuno returned with a bowl of hot soup, bread and cheese and Adam's knapsacks, rescued from the room he had been using before it was utilised for more wounded, did she discover how her husband had been wounded.

'Cesar!' she whispered, sitting back on her heels. 'A duel— are you sure?'

'Ask anyone, senhora. It is common knowledge. If I had not killed him, he would have shot the Major down in cold blood and everyone would have thought the French did it. I had to do it—I am not ashamed.'

'You are a brave and loyal friend,' she said. 'Will you be my friend too, Nuno? Help me get him away from here so that he can recover quickly and grow strong again?'

'So that you can break his heart again? Perhaps it would be better for him to die!'

The retort was so cruel—so totally unexpected—that Natália flinched as if he had struck her. Hostility was back in the boy's eyes as he gazed at her.

'Tomorrow I shall find a cart and we shall leave here,' he said at length. 'I shall drive, and you will care for him.

I do this for him, not for you, senhora. It would be better if you left before he is himself again. Let him forget you.'

'Forget—*Moça*?' Adam's voice was hoarse as he struggled up on one elbow. Fighting against the laudanum which dulled his brain, his hand groped unsteadily for Natália's dress. His fingers closed round the material, gripping it hard. 'Stay—I love you . . .'

He fell back to the ground, his senses leaving him again. With a cry, Natália gathered his head to her breast and pressed a tear-streaked cheek to his. He loved not her—not Natália—but the little servant-girl who had shared his bed! She knew now he would never return to Alto Verde and his wife. Slowly she raised her head and looked at Nuno.

'As soon as I know he is out of danger, I will go home. *A Moça* will cease to exist.'

The hard-fought battle of Bussaco had been so successful that it allowed Wellington to continue with his stratagem of a supposed retreat behind the Linhas de Torres Vedras—and Masséna, the eager fly anxious to avenge the defeat of his forces, followed unsuspectingly.

Very early in the morning of the 29th of September, while camp fires still flickered in the half light to deceive the enemy, the English began to withdraw from their positions. By the time it was light, the Coimbra road was packed with men and carts, cannon and horsemen.

Nuno, his bargaining-powers strained to the limit, had, after many unsuccessful hours of trudging from man to man, managed to sell the two horses Natália had given him which had once belonged to Drew and Alída. Natália had balked at parting with her sister's brooch and rings, but she had been prepared even for that in the last extreme if it meant being able to get Adam to safety.

All night long she had sat beside him, bathing his face, covering him when he constantly threw back the blanket in his delirium. The laudanum was wearing off, and the

pain that twisted his features as he was carefully lifted
into the waiting wagon was like the turning of a knife in
her heart. Scarcely had she climbed up beside him than
she was almost pushed to the floor as wounded men
hauled themselves in after her. Pilar screamed at them
and tried to push them away, but they kept coming,
dragging themselves up like mad animals. They knew
that to be left behind would mean certain death—
unpleasant death at the hands of the French. In desperation, Nuno whipped up the horses and Natália bent low
over Adam's body, with Pilar pressing tight against her,
her arms as tightly round him as she dared lest she hurt
him more, hiding her face as men were spilled backwards on to the ground. Vehement oaths and curses
followed them out of earshot. As it was, the cart was
overloaded, with a dozen men crammed on the small
floor, most with severed limbs or bloodstained bandages
round some part of their bodies.

The bundle of food Nuno had given them had been
tossed out in the mêlée to make more room, and Pilar
had managed to save only one water-bottle. She kept it
wedged firmly between her knees, hiding it with her
skirts from the others, and crouching low over Adam to
trickle a tiny amount surreptitiously between his lips
when it became necessary.

As the cart rumbled and jolted towards Coimbra,
Nuno, the beggar from the back streets of Lisboa, sat
hunched over the reins of the tired plodding mules,
praying for the first time in his young life to a God he had
never before acknowledged—begging silently, as tears
coursed down over his cheeks, for the life of Adam
Sorrell.

'What—what is happening?' Natália cried. Ahead of
them she could see smoke and flames leaping skywards.
Coimbra in flames! How could it be? The French were
close behind them, but it was not possible that they had

somehow managed to get ahead. Even the tall spires of the cathedral were obscured by drifting clouds of dense smoke. Both women crossed themselves as the men accompanying them came to their knees, the same terrible thought registering in their minds.

'I'll try to find a way round. Look at all those people ahead! We'll never get through,' Nuno said, turning the mules off the road. The cart lurched, and Adam gave a cry of agony. 'Hold him. Hold him tight! I must make a way through.'

Natália raised her head after a moment, and was horrified by the scene. Not even after the battle of Bussaco had she seen such utter chaos. People were streaming out of their houses, carrying whatever belongings they could manage. Children lost their mothers, and stood howling in the street until they were found or swept along in the growing tide of human bodies. It appeared to her as if every other building was on fire—and she saw soldiers with torches! The English were doing this! How could it be?

'Good old Nosey!' a wounded man beside her muttered, a smile lighting up his bearded face. 'That's the way to do it. Leave nothing for those blasted froggies!'

'They are burning people's homes,' Natália whispered, appalled. She had seen the scorched-earth policy for herself on the journey from Mafra to Sobral, but the devastation, the heartache of what it had entailed, the suffering to all concerned, did not come home to her until now.

'If you leave it, you'll have the French at the gates of Lisboa within a week. I haven't lost two brothers and my best friend fighting in this cursed war to let that happen,' another soldier muttered, scowling at her. 'Let 'em starve and die! And good riddance, I say. Then, maybe, I can go home to my wife and family. I've been here so long I'm beginning to forget what they look like!'

'Only 'cause you can't stand the look of your wife's

face,' someone else joked feebly, and Natália turned away in disgust. She could understand the necessity for what was being done, but she found no humour in it. Nor would the poor souls fleeing for their lives ahead of them, she suspected.

That night, when they made camp, Natália sat beside Nuno, watching the boy's face in the light of the flickering fire as she asked, 'What now?' She was no hardened soldier. She was afraid—for Adam as well as for herself and Pilar and yes—even for Nuno. He did not like her, of that she was sure, and in his young, impressionable mind he had good reason, but she trusted him with her own life and that of the man she loved. He would do nothing to jeopardise that!

'Soon we shall be in Torres Vedras,' came the quiet reply. 'There we leave these—others,' he jerked his head in the direction of the men who accompanied them. Only four remained now. Two had died on the way and been left by the wayside. 'If the Major does not have good medical attention, he will die. It is up to you. Perhaps it is your wish to pay him back for leaving you? If that is what is in your mind, I think I shall kill you!'

'If I did not care for him in that same way as you, then I—I would hit you,' Natália snapped, the thin reserve of her composure ready to snap from the strain of the past frightening hours. 'We shall take him to my sister's house in Mafra. There he will get well. From there I can write to his father to let him know he is safe and well.'

'Safe? Well?' Nuno stared at her almost contemptuously. 'Safe, perhaps. Well, he will never be after what you have done to him. Never have I known him to be taken with a woman as he was with you, and you betrayed his trust and his love!'

'You are mistaken,' she replied in a low fierce whisper as Adam stirred restlessly nearby, beads of sweat breaking out on his cheeks. 'He gave me nothing but a few minutes of his time. I gave him my love—something no other man has ever had or will have. He has destroyed me, foolish boy! When you have known love, you will understand that people not only gain from it, but also lose. I am the loser here. I carry inside me the child he will never acknowledge and never see, because by now I am probably not even his wife. He was rid of me as soon as possible. My words were lost on him—my pleading and my pride. I offered everything, and he rejected all. Yet I came after him—needed him, wanted so desperately to make him believe in me. And how did I do that? I dyed my skin and my hair and crawled into his bed like a common camp-follower.'

'Forgive me, senhora.' There was sudden pain in Nuno's brown eyes. 'I did not realise . . .'

'What a woman in love will do to be with her man? No, *moço*, you did not. No more did I until I was alone with his hatred and contempt. Now I have done all I can. I have no choice but to return home. Soon this dye will fade, and . . . I would go anyway, as soon as he is well. My father also is ill and I do not know how long he will live. I shall try to do for him what I have done for Adão—to make him as happy as I can in whatever time is available to me. You will say nothing of this to your master, do you understand me? Give me your solemn word.'

'I shall do nothing to hurt him, you know that,' the boy replied slowly. 'His happiness is my only concern.'

CHAPTER ELEVEN

Natália had been at Mafra for one week. She knew it was time to leave, and return to Alto Verde, on the morning that Adam opened his eyes for the first time and recognised her, and catching her by the hand, drew her down on the bed beside him and soundly kissed her. Such passion in that one kiss, which robbed him—them both—of breath! So much more eloquent than anything he could have said. His words at Bussaco still haunted her during sleepless nights.

'Stay, I love you!' If only she could! She had to leave—to disappear without a trace. He would forget in time, as he had forgotten the ardour he had shared with Natália in the fields one night. There would be others, she told herself. Women would flock round him when he went to Lisboa.

For seven long days she had nursed him, with little or no rest herself for the first four, until Adam's fever had broken and he had begun to sleep peacefully and regain his strength. She had sat patiently at his side, listening to his ramblings and often incoherent mutterings. She relived past battles with him in Spain, as he talked of places and people she had never heard of. She shared his agony of mind at the death of his brother, and wept many tears for the sister she would not see again. She held his hand when he tossed in the throes of fever, knowing there were times he was not aware of anyone being with him. She shrank from the venom in his voice when he suddenly began to talk of Alto Verde . . . and then, one week after they had returned to the house in Mafra, he opened his eyes and smiled up at her, and she knew he was going to live.

'What's wrong, *moça*? You look so solemn?' Adam asked, as she removed his breakfast tray and noted with satisfaction that he had managed to consume most of the food she had brought him.

'What could be wrong? You are getting well again. My prayers have been answered,' Natália answered, setting the tray down to make him more comfortable. When she went to draw away, his fingers were tight about one wrist.

'I told you not to care for me. If I had been killed . . .'

'But you were not,' she flashed. 'Besides, there are times when a woman has no choice in matters of the heart. It will all be decided for her. By fate.'

'Fate!' He gave a short laugh. 'Are you part gipsy, to believe in such things?'

'I only know that, if you had died, I would have died too—here.' Natália laid a hand against her breast. Leaving him would be like dying too, she thought, watching his long fingers caress the back of her skin.

The first thing he had done had been to get Nuno to shave him, sitting ill at ease in the huge carved bed while the boy wielded the razor. It was clear to Natália that he had never been so helpless before, and he did not like it!

As he moved restlessly, she watched his features pucker with pain, and said quickly, 'Let me help you to turn over. Perhaps I can ease a little of your discomfort.'

'I can think of many ways!' He gave her a wicked grin. He was fast becoming his old self again, she realised, as she moved him over on to his stomach. 'None of which I am capable of at the moment. In a few days . . .'

In a few days she would be gone, and out of his life for ever. But she would take with her the memories, and the child growing within her. His child! Their child! From the bedside cabinet she took the oil Pilar had given her when they first arrived. She had been using it on his skin to lessen the effect of the many scars he had sustained from the Bussaco battle. A musket ball had seared one shoulder, inflicting only slight damage, but leaving a deep red furrow on the bronzed skin. A Frenchman's sword had ripped open his jacket and left another two lines across his chest. His whole body, she discovered, had been covered with cuts and abrasions where he had slithered and fallen on the slopes in the first wild moments of the surprise attack—and from the fall he had sustained when his horse had been brought down beneath him.

All would heal in time. He would bear scars which were visible to the eye. Hers were not. Hers would never heal.

'You have magic hands, *moçu*!' Despite the pain she knew he still felt from the wound in his back, he began to relax as always beneath the slow, gentle motions of her hands. Gently she kneaded the firm flesh, smoothed the oil over the broad shoulders and down his back until her fingertips touched the swathing of bandages about his middle. Even touching him like this made her inwardly tremble, and she drew back.

'You must rest. The doctor will be here in a little while.'

'This afternoon, I think I shall get up for a while,' Adam declared, as she settled the pillow comfortably beneath his head.

'You will not! You are too weak.'

'You are beginning to sound more like my wife than my . . .'

'Bedmate? Mistress?' She stepped back, eyes flashing.

'What is it? Why are you angry?' He frowned at the unexpected bitterness in her voice. 'Don't you know you mean more to me than anyone in this world?' The knife turned again inside her. Adam's eyes, suddenly grave and penetrating, searched her face. 'It is strange how, when I dream, it is her face I see—her pale-skinned body I hold in my arms—yet she gave me nothing. It is you who give me comfort. With you I have found love.'

'In time, you will no doubt discard me as you did her!'

'*Bastante!* I will not take that, even from you.' The pale eyes glittered angrily.

'I am sorry, Adão. I did not mean . . . I am so tired.' She turned and ran from the room in tears. She could not remain in the house for another day!

'Well? You have done it?' Natália turned anxiously on Pilar when she came into the kitchen. She was supervising the preparation of nourishing broth for Adam's lunch. The last duty she would ever perform for him. She had sent the woman out to hire a carriage to take her back to Alto Verde. While he was eating, she intended to slip out of the house unseen and take flight. In a few days, Pilar would request permission to return to her old home.

'*Sim.* A carriage will be waiting in the *praça* at one o'clock. I had to pay extra. The driver said he earns more money here, using his vehicle for the English officers, than going so far away.'

'Far away? He will be back by nightfall and well able to earn himself some more money if it pleases him,' Natália retorted indignantly. She could have used Alída's small carriage, but its absence would be noticed and the driver questioned immediately he returned to the house—and her whereabouts revealed. She must simply disappear, and this seemed the easiest way. 'Good! I shall go and rest for a while.'

'You cannot,' Pilar protested, looking agitated. She crossed herself several times. 'Senhor Charles is here. He could not have received the letter you sent because he has just come from Sobral—and he has someone with him. *Menina, Sua Excelêcia* Wellington himself has come to see Major Sorrell! I have put them in the sitting-room, and given them wine.'

Charles Sorrell and Wellington! Natália's tiredness vanished in an instant.

'Is that all the hospitality we can offer them? Find them food, and the best claret! And have a bottle of brandy brought from the cellars.'

Adam, who had just begun to doze, was startled by the whirlwind which swept into the room and began to tidy it.

'You have visitors! Your father—and the General himself! Downstairs. Sit up and let me make you look presentable.'

'Dammit, *moça*, do you think I'm going to receive Lord Wellington sitting up in bed like a blasted invalid?' he said sharply, as she smoothed the bed-covers. 'Help me up. And call Nuno to come and dress me. No, you can do it, it will be quicker. My clothes—where are they?'

'In the closet, but . . . you are not well enough! To sit in a chair, perhaps.' The pale eyes which came to rest on her quelled further argument. 'Be it on your own head. What do I care if your wound opens!'

In an angry silence she found his clothes and helped him into them, watching apprehensively as his mouth tightened with the pain of every movement and a pallor returned to his cheeks which had she had hoped never to see again.

'Your arm, *moça*,' he said firmly. It was an order, not a request, and meekly she slipped her arm through his and helped him to negotiate the narrow flight of stairs which led downstairs. She would have turned back at the doorway, but he retained a tight hold on her and she was propelled firmly into the room.

'Adam, my boy! Is this a miracle? Pilar told me you were confined to bed.'

Charles came striding across the room to clasp his hand. For a long moment, father and son embraced each other, silently acknowledging the grief they carried inside them at the death of Drew, and comforted by the contact until they could be alone to talk and ease the pain.

'Sit down before you fall,' Natália pleaded, as Adam swayed unsteadily, the blood draining from his face.

'As you can see, I have a good nurse,' he said drily.

'Who tenders excellent advice!' The man who rose from a chair in front of them still wore the same large grey great-coat as when he had directed the cannon fire on the heights of Bussaco. On a table lay the plain cocked hat. Although she had seen him several times in the camps, Natália had never before been so close to the man who had sworn to free Portugal from Franch domination. She found herself scrutinised by sharp, brilliant, light-blue eyes. A frank appraisal was being made of her, and he did not care if she knew it. He had strong, intelligent features without the often annoying arrogance which accompanied wealth and rank—and power. For the first time, she fully understood the magnitude of this man. Had she been a soldier under his command, she would have trusted him implicitly, and followed him anywhere.

A smile warmed the dark face as he took Adam's hand and soundly shook it. 'I'm glad to see you on your feet again. Don't stand on ceremony, that's not the way it is with us! Sit down and have a glass of brandy. It is excellent. Do you know it's raining outside? Torrents of the filthy stuff!' He gave a short laugh. 'Just what we need, eh?'

'I think divine providence is on your side,' Adam replied, managing a smile as he sank gratefully into a comfortable chair. Natália tried to hide her surprise at the familiarity between the two men. It was obvious that the Viscount considered Adam more than just another officer.

Charles looked from one to the other in puzzlement. 'May I ask what is going on? The roads are flooded—if it continues to rain, they will be unusable.'

'Exactly.' Wellington and Adam spoke in unison.

'Good heavens! The French will be bogged down until spring! Our men have the safety and protection of the lines, but the enemy have nothing but scorched earth. No food—and glorious, glorious rain. Oh, how it rains in Portugal! They will not be able to reach Lisboa.'

'They were never meant to, Father. It was all part of an ingenious plan of his lordship's, but until now we did not know if it would work.'

'Only a select few of my officers knew anything about it,' Wellington said, indicating that Adam was, indeed, high in his esteem. 'I think others now are beginning to see the light.' He once more picked up his glass and savoured the contents. 'Another three days should have my men exactly where I want them—deployed from Torres Vedras to the Atlantic. And the Tagus and southwards to protect the capital itself. If necessary, I shall sit out the winter and let the men have a well-earned rest. If the old fox Masséna hasn't given up and gone home by then, we shall oblige him one last time.'

'Your visit is appreciated, sir. You know that,' Adam said, well pleased by the news.

'As is your courage and bravery—Colonel Sorrell.' Natália caught her breath in delight. Charles beamed as the General took an envelope from the inside of his great-coat and laid it on the table beside Adam's chair. 'I wanted to bring you the good news myself, and to tell you that your *guerrilleros* have arrived in Mafra. My visit is a small reward for all you have done. If only I had a dozen men with your capabilities!' Wellington said smilingly, and Natália was instantly touched by the sincerity in the quiet tones. Briefly he clasped Adam's hand for a second time. 'Grow fit and strong again, Colonel. I shall have need of you, come spring. I must leave you now, but I hope to see you again soon. I think a little celebration is in order, gentlemen? A dinner, a ball, perhaps—and, of course, you are both invited.'

'I may not be able to dance, but I'll break a bottle with you, sir,' Adam replied. 'We accept, of course.'

'Not for the first time, eh? Good man! What's this I hear of you having a wife hidden away somewhere in these hills? Bring her too, I'd like to meet the woman who has infiltrated your impenetrable defences!'

'Thank you,' It took Adam a moment to recover his composure. 'I'll do my best to see that she is with me.'

Minutes passed before Natália realised that Wellington had left the room. Charles, who had escorted him to the door, came back and stood before his son's chair questioningly. He dared not look at Natália. He had not given her more than a cursory glance since the moment she entered—he was afraid he would give himself away. He could feel her uneasiness and growing frustration. How had she managed it? Was it possible that Adam did not know her? She was thin, and tired from days of constantly nursing him, and her skin appeared lighter to him than when they had parted, although with the high-fastening, long-sleeved dress she wore, it was successfully hidden. But not the eyes. Not those exquisite, wonderfully expressive blue eyes.

'Were you serious?' He replenished his glass of red wine. 'Would you care for some of this? Good for the blood and, from what I hear, you lost plenty on the way here.'

'I shall have plenty of time to make it up when I come to Lisboa. I should be able to travel in a few more days. You must stay until then, and we can get very drunk together. I've been meaning to since Drew—died—but . . .' Adam broke off with a grimace. 'I'll have a brandy. That's good for the blood, too—or so you always told me.'

'Do you think that's a good idea?' Natália's protest faded as he looked up at her, and something in the depth of those grey-green eyes warned her that he did not welcome this show of possessiveness.

'Am I serious about what?'

'Bringing Natália to Mafra. In Lisboa, before you left . . .'

Adam swallowed some brandy and felt a fire ignite in his stomach, but after a moment the pain in his back and chest was dulled and he swallowed the other half. He needed to talk to his father. There were so many things to be sorted out. Problems of his own making . . . Well, not all his own.

'Will you arrange for a room to be made ready for my father, moça. Have we enough food in the house for another mouth?'

'Probably. If not, I shall go shopping this afternoon.'

'No, send Pilar to me. You get some rest.'

'Did you do as I asked?' she heard Adam say as she slowly closed the door after her, lingering as long as possible. Why did she feel he wished to be rid of her?

'At once . . . Have you told her yet?'

'In good time . . . There are many things to be settled yet. There is no hurry—not now.'

There was no doubt in Natália's mind what they were discussing. The first and most important thing always on Adam's mind—the annulment of their marriage. And Charles had arranged it, even though he knew of her love. How could he have been so cruel? The answer was simple. He loved his son above her. What could be more natural? She had gained nothing from the deception except to confirm her husband's continued contempt for her and his willingness to forget her in the arms of another woman. Squaring her shoulders, she turned away and went upstairs.

A few minutes before one o'clock, she slipped out of the house by a back door and hurried towards the praça, her heart in her mouth for fear the carriage would not be there. It was. Tears blurred her vision as much as the blinding rain. She climbed inside and pulled the heavy shawl away from her face and shook the rain-spots from her skirts. She would not be missed for some while, she was confident of that. On the pretence of going to her room to rest, she had left the housekeeper to serve Charles and Adam with their lunch. Afterwards they would probably rest. Perhaps it would be late afternoon before he wondered where she was. And when he did? No—she must think of him no more!

How tired she was! She would try to sleep on the short journey home. She needed her strength to sustain the life inside her, even though she felt as if it had all drained from her.

'Drive on!' she called up to the waiting man. Her voice was so choked with emotion that she had to repeat the order.

Natália gave an alarmed cry as she was rudely awakened from her sleep and thrown roughly across the opposite seat. She could hear the driver cursing as he fought to control the horses. The carriage slithered precariously on the mud-drenched road, and came to a halt. Ruefully rubbing a bruised shoulder, she resumed her seat and looked out of the window to see what was happening. She froze in horror at the figures who surrounded the carriage. She recognised them immediately as Adam's *guerrilleros*. Five of them, and staring at her in none too friendly a manner, and talking to the driver—Nuno! Dear heaven, what was going on? Adam had sent them after her, but why? And how had he discovered her absence so quickly? Pilar! No one else could have betrayed her. She could not believe her lifelong friend and adviser would fail her!

The door was swung open. Nuno kneed his horse closer and peered inside. The young face staring at her was without expression. 'You will please to dismount and come with us.'

'I will not! How dare you stop me. Get out of my way

at once! That is an order,' she cried angrily. She could not—she would not—go back!

'And who do you think you are, to be giving us orders? Only the Major does that, and he told us to bring you back by any means necessary. Do you understand me?' one of the *guerrilleros* interrupted.

'He—he said that?' Natália shrank back in her seat as another of the men dismounted and came to the door, glaring at her warningly.

'Stealing to survive is one thing, my girl. Stealing from a man who has befriended you, fed you, given you more than any other man, I'll warrant—is another! Women like you are flogged raw in my village and sent packing! Get down.'

When Natália still hesitated, he reached in and grasped her by the arm, to pull her bodily from the seat. Her shawl was wound unceremoniously about her head and shoulders, and despite futile struggles, she was lifted up in front of one of the *guerrilleros*. An arm went tightly about her waist, almost squeezing the breath from her body.

'I shall have every one of you whipped for this!' she began.

Her words were drowned in the howls of laughter that came from her companions. Miserably, she lapsed into silence. She was being taken back to Mafra, and she could do nothing about it! The *guerrilleros* wheeled their horses about, and at a fast pace headed back towards the town.

The door of the sitting-room closed behind her, leaving Natália alone with the silent man standing at the window, his back towards her. She was soaking wet, and water dripped from the hem of her dress to form a puddle about her sandalled feet. She was cold, too, and shivering, but she did not know if it was from the dreadful ride she had been forced to endure or from her fear of what was to happen.

Adam turned, and had to harden his heart at the sight of the bedraggled spectacle. Not yet . . . He wanted to be sure. Of her—not of himself. He had known from the very beginning that there would never be another woman in his life. He had refused to accept it then—now it was different. He would keep her with him, even if he had to lock her in her room!

'I have stolen nothing from you,' Natália cried tremulously. The gaze of those glittering eyes was unnerving.

'I know. Take off that wet shawl and sit down. We have things to discuss,' Adam replied coolly, totally in command of the situation. She had no idea of how his heart had somersaulted with the unsteadiness of a young boy as she was pushed into the room. His men had not been too gentle with her, but they had brought her back. That was all that mattered.

'Then how dare you have me brought back like—like a common thief! You don't own me.' Attack was her only defence. To make him so angry that he would send her away willingly—at once.

Adam's eyes narrowed sharply. He poured himself some brandy, and red wine for her. She shook her head when he offered it, and he shrugged and put it down beside her. Reaching out, he pulled the shawl from her shoulders and tossed it into a chair.

'That's better! Now I can see your face.' He stood before her, feet slightly apart, one hand thrust deep into the pockets of his trousers, the other holding the brandy balloon, the contents of which he sampled slowly, every moment of silence prolonging her agony. It was an easy stance, and there was even a slight smile on his features as he surveyed the black curls pressed against her cheeks, the quivering lips, the hands clasped tightly together before her, but she knew his mind was active, searching for some explanation, and she had none to give. Except the truth!

She looked for all the world like a frightened servant-girl waiting to be reprimanded for some misdemeanour, Adam thought. Was her fear really of him—after all they had shared? Could he have been wrong again?

'I lost you once through my own stupidity. I have no intention of making the same mistake again! As for stealing from me, that was the truth. You stole my heart at Alto Verde, and again at Sobral. And I do own you, Natália. You are still my wife!'

The quiet words came at her like a thunderbolt, rocking her on her feet. She gave a cry and pressed her hands over her mouth, her eyes widening.

Ruthlessly Adam continued with the advantage her confusion gave him. 'You presented yourself to me as a waif who did not even have a name of her own, yet your skin when you came to my bed that first night had been freshly bathed and perfumed, and your clothes were scrupulously clean. Your hands, although they should have been rough and calloused by work, were soft —because you have always put salve on them at night and I suspect you continued to do so. Really, my dear, Pilar let you down there. Did she not tell you that men notice such things? At least I do. I should not be alive now if I had not trained myself to use every sense I possess!'

Pilar! Had he forced her to tell him everything, or had she supplied the information willingly? What did it matter . . . He knew. Now he would reject her again as he had done at Alto Verde. He did not love his girl any more than he had loved Natália—he had lied to her, tricked her. She swayed unsteadily, but drew back when he put out a hand to help her. He ignored the blue fire beginning to glow in her eyes. She was growing angry, and that was what he wanted. Now there would be truth between them, once and for all.

'You noticed all these things . . .' And the dye too, she thought, which she had remembered too late! 'You said nothing. How you must hate me! You were a beast to let me throw myself at you!'

'I heard no complaints . . . and I had none. Besides, I wanted to find out what your game was. I thought you had some crazy notion of revenge in your head for what had happened between us at Alto Verde. Did you really believe I would not know you? My own wife?' He flung the words at her, a contemptuous twist to his lips.

'I was not your wife—not really. No more than I am now.'

'It took me a long time to realise what lengths you would go to in order to have a child—to please your father.'

Natália gasped at the cruel words. 'I didn't follow you . . . for that.'

'Why else? To prove to me your undying love? I didn't believe you at Alto Verde, so why should I now?' Adam hurled the taunt at her mercilessly, and the final insult snapped the thin thread of her temper.

Her hand lashed out at his face, connected with the balloon he held and sent it shattering against the panelled wall. Adam's lean fingers coupled her wrist. His free hand clamped hard down upon her shoulders, and she was dragged against his chest. The glittering look in his eyes made her feel quite faint as he forced her face up to his, and his mouth descended on hers. He kissed her as he had kissed her that night at Alto Verde, before misunderstandings and a forced marriage parted them and substituted hatred in his heart for the love he had found in that ecstatic moment. He knew now that he had never really hated her. She had proved that when she came to him in her disguise, and he had lost himself in the worship of her body, silenting accepting he might one day lose her again, but unable to reject what she offered. Paradise, indeed, for a man who had never known love and often denied that any woman could be totally faithful to one man.

Natália's senses reeled, clamoured for more. She clung to him as he moved her backwards to the couch and lowered her, the hardness of his body settled over her, holding her fast. He brushed the wet curls from her cheeks and kissed them, trailed gentle kisses down over her throat as his hands explored her body beneath the material of her dress.

'What are you?' he whispered against her ear. 'Nátalia or *moça*? Wife or mistress?'

Natália opened her eyes and smiled up at him. Her long fingers touched his cheek briefly, then the firm line of his mouth, and then nestled in the dark hair curling about his neck.

'Whatever you wish me to be . . . Wife or mistress, it matters not, so long as I am with you. But . . .' Tears sprang to her eyes as she remembered the conversation she had overheard. 'I—I am not your wife any more, am I? Charles has had the marriage annulled. I heard . . .'

Adam cursed gently at the utter misery in her eyes. '*Idiota!* The moment I realised who you were . . .' At her gasp of surprise, a second curse broke from his lips and then a half-smile, to acknowledge how successfully she had deceived even him. 'Very well, you fooled me for a day or two only—after which, I wrote to my father at once to rescind my previous request. He had told me everything. I tried to be angry with him, but how could I? If he had not helped you on your way, perhaps you might never have reached Sobral and we would not have spent so many enjoyable nights together.'

'Why?' Natália asked softly. He loved her. It was in his voice, his touch, his eyes. He had looked at her like this at Alto Verde, but in her innocence she had not recognised it as love. 'Tell me, Adão. Let me hear it from your lips for me . . . For Natália, not *moça*. For the girl you married.'

'Enchantress! I love you. I would have told you that night, had we not been interrupted. I should have gone to your father and asked to marry you.'

'And Cesar would have challenged you, and you would have discovered how foolish I had been! I did not mean to deceive you, but I—I thought you were only flirting with me, that you did not even regard me as a woman . . . I would not forget you as I thought you would me—the moment you left.'

'I would have fought him to have you, as I shall fight any man who even smiles at you after today. I am a very possessive man!'

'Forgive me?'

'Everyone is entitled to be foolish at some time in their lives!' Adam kissed her again, drawing an instant response from her eager lips. He cursed the injury which prevented him from carrying her upstairs and showing her the depths of his love. They were both free of the past now, of the misfortunes they had inadvertently brought upon themselves. They had all the time in the world to discover the wonder of their love.

'When I am better . . .' he warned teasingly, as her hand slid inside his shirt against the warmth of his chest and his skin began to burn like fire at the slight touch.

Her eyes bright with love, Natália took his hand and laid it against her stomach. 'Make haste, *meu amor*! We do not have very much time . . .'

'Colonel and Mrs Sorrell.'

At the announcement, many heads in the crowded ballroom turned to stare at the newly-arrived couple—a tall and handsome man in a blue uniform trimmed with gold, and the slender, exquisitely gowned young woman at his side. Fans fluttered and conversation buzzed as the couple began to make their way towards Viscount Wellington, whose elevation to an earldom was already being hinted at by gossip.

Natália's gown was of white tulle over a white satin underdress. It was cut very low across her breasts, with small puff sleeves that left her arms bare. Jewels flashed at her throat and in her ears: Adam's betrothal gifts, a magnificent sapphire necklace and earrings to match the brilliance of her eyes. Her skin glowed with colour in the candlelight, for not all the dye had been erased from her skin despite Pilar's efforts. Adam, himself, had soundly scrubbed her, and they had both ended up wet and laughing in each other's arms.

The short hair, with which they had had more success, was swept high on the crown of her head in a mass of red-gold curls and surmounted by a diamond tiara—her husband's wedding present. She moved with a grace and elegance which made her the envy of every woman, and attracted the eyes of every man, but the hand laid upon Adam's sleeve trembled slightly. This night was the culmination of all her dreams—and it was only the beginning. Somewhere in the sea of faces were Charles and her father, whose health had improved sufficiently for him to come and stay at the house. Had the news of an impending grandson had anything to do with it? she wondered. If it had, she was too happy to mind. She and Adam were all he had. If she could bring a little more happiness into his lonely life by giving his dream, too, then she would do so.

Adam's dark head bent towards her, a reassuring smile warmed the bronzed features, and the love and pride blazing in his eyes dispelled her nervousness.

Before the General and a dozen of his fellow officers, they halted. Adam's hand again covered the slender fingers on his arm. His quiet voice, vibrating with emotion such as she had never heard expressed so openly before, spoke the words Natália had thought never to hear—acknowledging her for the first time.

'My Lord—Gentlemen. I have the honour to present to you my wife, Natália.'